A Primer on
STATISTICS *for* BUSINESS
and ECONOMICS

A Primer on

The Primer series is under the editorial supervision of

PETER L. BERNSTEIN

STATISTICS *for* BUSINESS *and* ECONOMICS

Irwin Miller

Arthur D. Little, Inc. and
Boston University

 RANDOM HOUSE *New York*

TO *JoAnn*

Preface

NOT ONLY THE STUDY OF ECONOMICS but also the entire field of financial and business management have entered a new era—one in which the ingredients for success include the ability to use many of the theories and techniques of modern science. The modern economist is the product of a discipline that requires lengthy and deep studies of mathematics and the sciences. Applications of statistics, operations research, and other technical methods have pervaded business and industrial management. Witness the number of engineers, physicists, and other scientists who now are emerging as corporate leaders.

Among the modern scientific techniques that have made the strongest impact on economics as well as management is statistics. The modern economist has his hands tied if he attempts to do economic research, to make economic forecasts, or even to understand the literature in his own field without a knowledge of statistics. The modern industrial manager is constantly being bombarded with evaluations and recommendations for expansion, marketing, new-product development, and so forth, which are couched in the language of statistics. He can hardly make an intelligent decision regarding the worth of these studies and recommendations if he does not have at least a basic appreciation of the underlying statistical concepts.

The purpose of this primer is to introduce the reader primarily concerned with problems of economics and business decision-making to the basic statistical ideas and methods now prevailing. It is written for the intelligent and interested reader who probably has had a course in algebra, but who took the course many years ago and wasn't terribly excited about it even then. To this end, I have put the emphasis on ideas rather than details and formulas. Enough techniques are illustrated, by means of examples of potential interest in business and economics, to put some meat on the bones of these ideas. When you finish reading this book, you won't be a statistician, but, hopefully, you will have a better idea of what statisticians are talking about.

I would like to express my deepest appreciation to my many colleagues at Arthur D. Little, Inc., who have read portions of the manuscript and have given me the benefit of their perceptive comments, notably John Odle and Gary Watts. I would also like to thank Peter Bernstein for his courtesy, understanding, and his extremely valuable editorial suggestions, and Mrs. Alice Sahagen for her remarkably accurate typing and proofreading.

I. M.
Cambridge, Massachusetts

Contents

1 / *Introduction*   3

2 / *Figures Never Lie (But Liars Sometimes Figure)*   7

Tables and Pictures   8
Frequency Distributions   16
Graphs of Frequency Distributions   21

3 / *The Average Game*   27

What Kind of Average?   28
Calculating Averages—Raw Data   32
Calculating the Mean—Grouped Data   34

4 / *Departures From the Average*   39

Measurement of Variability   41
Calculating Standard Deviations from Grouped Data   45
Interpreting the Standard Deviation   48

5 / *Taking a Chance*   53

What Are Probabilities?   54
How Do Probabilities Behave?   59
Prior Probabilities and the Rule of Bayes   66

6 / *Alligator Pears and Distributed Ignorance* 73

Probability Distributions 75
The Binomial Distribution 78
The Poisson Distribution 88
The Normal Distribution 93

7 / *Decisions, Decisions, Decisions* 103

Random Samples 104
The Sample Mean 107
Estimating a Population Mean 113
A Confidence Game 115
Putting It to the Test 118
Understanding the Polls 123
Bayesian Inference—Use of Prior Information 129

8 / *The Numbers Game* 133

Selection of Index Items 136
Weighted Averages 139
Construction of Index Numbers 143

9 / *The Crystal Ball* 149

Fitting a Line 150
Correlation 156
Economic Time Series 160

BIBLIOGRAPHY 171

INDEX 173

A Primer on
STATISTICS *for* BUSINESS
and ECONOMICS

CHAPTER 1

Introduction

In this primer we shall introduce statistics from the business and economics point of view. This statement needs clarification. We do not plan to dwell on specific economic data or even special "economic statistics" such as the consumer price index or the value of the farm surplus. We intend, instead, to attempt to discover how we should interpret economic statistics, so that we may better understand and use them.

The term "statistics" is one of the more confusing technical words that has come into daily usage. Perhaps it is because "statistics" really has two rather distinct meanings; in its first meaning it is plural and in its second it is singular. "Statistics" in its *plural* meaning refers to a collection of numerical information. Closely associated with this first meaning is the art of summarization and presentation of statistics, known as *descriptive statistics.*

"Statistics" in its *singular* meaning does not refer to collections of data themselves, but denotes the art and science of interpreting, and drawing inferences from, certain special kinds of data collections, called samples. (In Chapter 7 we shall have more to say about "samples" and the "populations" that they are supposed to represent.)

The greatest and most widespread efforts at collecting accurate and reliable statistics have been made in connection with government and economic affairs. We are all at least partially familiar with the vast collection of economic and business statistics published both by governmental organizations and by private enterprise. The Bureau of the Census collects statistics concerning the population of the United States and maintains a storehouse of these statistics. The Bureau of Labor Statistics compiles data concerning wage rates, unemployment, and prices, to name a few examples.

According to legend, the compilation of statistics got its start when some otherwise unsung monarch asked about the capability of his subjects to pay taxes. First he asked how many subjects he had and where they lived, and the science of demography had its beginnings. Then he asked about their earnings and their prospects for future earnings, and economic statistics began to be compiled. In fact, it is hard to see how any really viable government could exist without regularly collecting comprehensive and reasonably accurate statistics concerning the status and disposition of the governed.

This early and inevitable association between the state and information about the state gave statistics its name. A person who was an expert in the field of state information was called a *statist,* a term now obsolete.

Historically, statistics as a science grew from two very disparate sources. From the statists, who were faced with the problem of condensing and interpreting the vast collections of data that they were amassing, the methods and techniques of descriptive statistics began to emerge. During the eighteenth century mathematicians began to study problems originally posed by gamblers, and the theory of probability was developed. (We shall introduce the elements of this theory in Chapter 5.) Thus, we can view the modern science of statistics as the wedding of these two influences. Statistics is a living science, changing constantly in its content and its methods to meet the special needs of its many fields of application.

Now let us begin our tour of this amazingly versatile field, which has only recently begun its process of adaptation to the needs of business and economics, and which has already accomplished so much.

CHAPTER 2

Figures Never Lie
(But Liars Sometimes Figure)

Statistics are dull and lifeless to most people, but they must have some importance, otherwise why would there be so many? As history gives perspective and direction to the present and the future, statistical records are needed to help govern current affairs and long-range planning. But raw, overvoluminous and undigested numerical facts *are* dull and lifeless. Statistical data need to be organized and, if necessary, condensed if we are to glean useful information from them.

The art of data organization, condensation, and presentation is called descriptive statistics. Data have been properly organized and presented if the results are understandable, the essential content of the information is preserved, and if the meaning and interpretation of the data have not been biased or distorted. It is all too easy to fail in achieving one or more of these desiderata through carelessness or lack of training. Can you imagine what can be done on purpose to distort the meaning of statistical data? Intentional distortions are too frequent not to have escaped public notice: Witness the often-heard remarks: "One can prove anything with statistics" and "Figures never lie, but liars sometimes figure."

The plain fact is that one can prove nothing with statistics. Hopefully, we shall discover (when we discuss inferential statistics) that we can use statistics to determine only whether data are consistent or inconsistent with a previously stated hypothesis. But more about this later; for now, let us concentrate on the rudiments of descriptive statistics in the hope that we can learn to avoid being bored as well as misled with statistics.

Tables and Pictures

Table 1 presents figures concerning tax revenues.

Notice that this table has each of the following ingredients: a *title* that states exactly and as succinctly as possible what the entries are; *units of measurement* (dollars, in this case); a set of *row captions* (in this case, years) that acts as an index to distinguish each member of the series from the others; and, finally, a set of *column captions* that distinguishes one body of related data in the table from another.

In general, when we look at a table of statistics, we should insist that it show exactly what each entry denotes. We can relieve our lives of much tedium and

TABLE *1* / *Governmental Per Capita Tax Revenue*
(*Dollars*)

Year	State and Local[a]	Federal[b]	Total
1942[c]	63.24	90.94	154.18
1950[c]	104.92	231.98	336.90
1955[c]	142.09	348.45	490.54
1960	200.66	427.81	628.47
1962	223.62	442.69	666.32
1963	233.35	460.18	693.53
1964	249.75	473.03	722.78
1965	266.11	483.49	749.61

[a] Estimates subject to sampling variation.

[b] Includes excess profits tax, normal tax, and surtax. For 1942 includes unjust enrichment tax.

[c] Excludes Alaska and Hawaii.

SOURCE: Extracted from U.S. Bureau of the Census, *Statistical Abstract of the United States: 1966*, 87th ed. (Washington, D.C., 1966), p. 417.

add some badly needed free time to our overcrowded schedules if we eliminate all other statistics from further consideration.

Even a perfectly adequate table can be difficult to assimilate. No matter how well they are presented, columns of figures are columns of figures; if a picture is worth a thousand words, imagine how many numbers it can replace. Charts and graphs are commonly used to present statistical information; they give us at a glance the essential meaning of a collection of statistics.

The *pie chart* is a useful method of showing the proportions into which a whole quantity has been divided. The sizes (central angles) of the pie-shaped wedges in Figure 1 are proportional to the percentages into which categories of the 1967 federal administrative

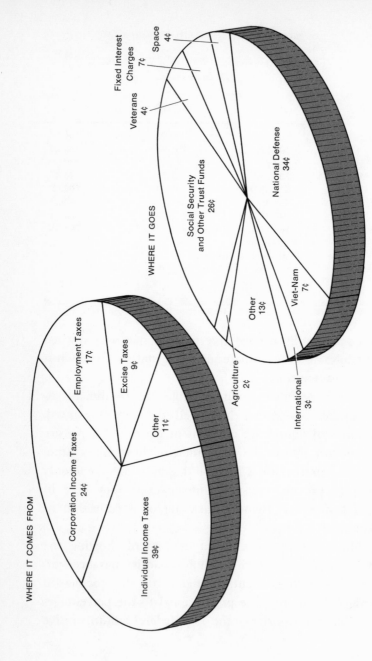

FIGURE 1 / The Federal Government Dollar: 1967

SOURCE: U.S. Bureau of the Census, *Statistical Abstract of the United States: 1966.* 87th ed. (Washington, D.C., 1966), p. 387.

budget have been allocated. Note the clever use of the dollar as the unit; instead of showing the total amount of money in the 1967 budget, these charts show only how it is divided among sources of receipts and categories of expenditures. A direct comparison of the 1967 budget with that of a preceding year is possible, even though the totals differ in amount.

The *bar chart* provides a rapid visual comparison of the relative frequency of related statistics. The heights of the bars shown in the bar chart in Figure 2 are proportional to the percentages of draftees that fall into each of the named categories.

The *graph* is an ideal way to summarize purely quantitative information. An example of an excellent graph is shown in Figure 3; it is uncluttered and interpretable at a glance. For those who want detailed figures, a table supporting this graph appears right along with it. This figure comes from the *Life Insurance Fact Book* for 1966, published by the Institute of Life Insurance. (This little annual contains many examples of unusually well prepared statistical tables, charts, and graphs.) Note that all scales are clearly marked, the vertical scale starts from zero, and it is unbroken.

Sometimes the vertical scale of a graph must be started at some value other than zero; otherwise full use would not be made of the allowable space. When this is done, great care must be exercised to avoid giving the wrong impression. Figure 4 shows a good example of this technique; the scales are clearly marked and the results are not misleading. In Figure 5, however, we have taken a small portion of the data supporting Fig-

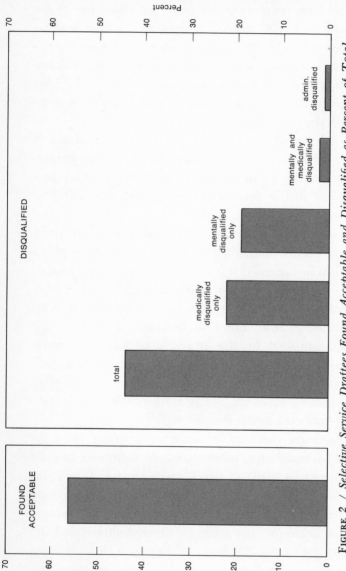

FIGURE 2 / *Selective Service Draftees Found Acceptable and Disqualified as Percent of Total Examined: 1965*

SOURCE: U.S. Bureau of the Census, *Statistical Abstract of the United States: 1966.* 87th ed. (Washington, D.C., 1966), p. 250. Data from Department of the Army, Office of the Surgeon General.

Year	Ordinary	Group	Industrial	Credit
1920	$1,990	$ 960	$150	$200
1925	2,270	1,340	170	220
1930	2,460	1,700	210	200
1935	2,160	1,590	220	180
1940	2,130	1,700	240	150
1945	2,100	1,930	270	170
1950	2,320	2,480	310	360
1955	2,720	3,200	350	530
1956	2,850	3,360	360	530
1957	3,040	3,580	370	580
1958	3,220	3,740	380	610
1959	3,420	3,870	390	680
1960	3,590	4,030	390	720
1961	3,760	4,160	400	740
1962	3,930	4,320	420	800
1963	4,130	4,490	420	820
1964	4,380	4,630	430	860
1965	4,660	5,050	450	900

Sources: Spectator Year Book and Institute of Life Insurance.

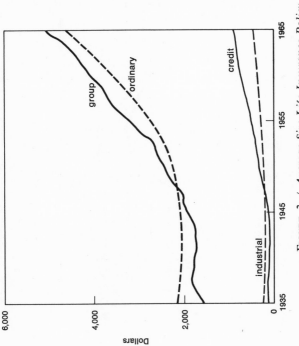

FIGURE 3 / *Average Size Life Insurance Policy in Force in the United States*

SOURCE: *Life Insurance Fact Book* (New York: Institute of Life Insurance, 1966), p. 22.

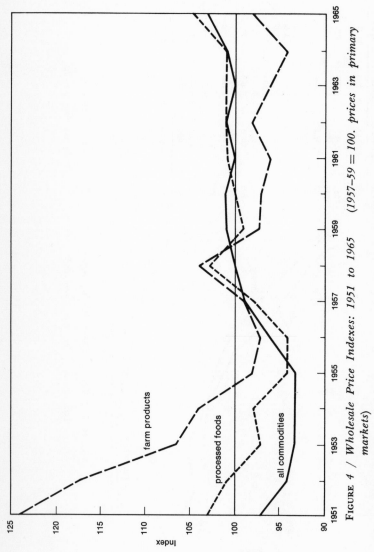

FIGURE 4 / *Wholesale Price Indexes: 1951 to 1965* (1957–59 = 100. *prices in primary markets*)

SOURCE: U.S. Bureau of the Census, *Statistical Abstract of the United States: 1966.* 87th ed. (Washington, D.C., 1966), p. 348.

ure 4 and presented the false impression of a phenom-
enal rise in the wholesale price index during 1965.
Here is an example of how choice of scale can radically
change the impression given by a graph.

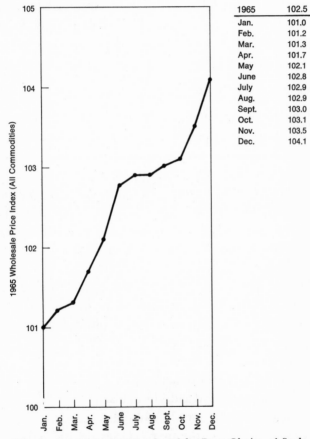

1965	102.5
Jan.	101.0
Feb.	101.2
Mar.	101.3
Apr.	101.7
May	102.1
June	102.8
July	102.9
Aug.	102.9
Sept.	103.0
Oct.	103.1
Nov.	103.5
Dec.	104.1

FIGURE 5 / *Distortion Produced by Poor Choice of Scale*

SOURCE: Adapted from U.S. Bureau of the Census, *Statistical Abstract
of the United States: 1966.* 87th ed. (Washington, D.C., 1966), p.
348.

There are other, far more flagrant deceptions that can be practiced with graphs. Trend lines sometimes are drawn through highly variable data that may exhibit a trend only in the imagination of the person making the graph. Worse, such trends sometimes are extrapolated beyond the range of the available data. One more word of caution—beware of the graph having axes that are not labeled!

Frequency Distributions

The bar chart of Figure 2 shows the percentage of observations corresponding to each of several qualities or attributes, and it is an example of a *categorical distribution*. If data are grouped according to numerical size rather than category, we have a *numerical distribution*. A frequency table, or *frequency distribution*, is a table that divides numerical data into a relatively small number of classes, listing the number of observations in each class.

One of the first steps in summarizing a long list of statistical data often consists of constructing a frequency table. To illustrate, let us consider the data of Table 2, showing 140 closing prices (February 24, 1967) selected at random from all common stocks listed on the New York Stock Exchange.

First, we need to decide how many classes to use in constructing the frequency table. As a general rule, the more data we have, the more classes we use; however, it is rarely helpful to use fewer than 5 or more than 15

TABLE 2 / *Closing Price of 140 Stocks, N.Y.S.E., February 24, 1967*

40 1/4	42 5/8	19 1/8	28 3/8	17 3/8	19	60 1/8
32 3/4	32	16 1/4	48 1/2	46 3/4	69 1/4	18 1/2
17 3/8	40 5/8	61 1/4	61 1/2	67 3/4	53 5/8	17 3/8
85 1/2	52 5/8	8 3/4	34 1/2	14 5/8	44	77 3/8
77 1/8	15 7/8	41 1/4	18 7/8	27 1/2	31 3/8	21 3/8
31 1/4	31 1/8	26 5/8	32 1/2	93 3/4	16	21
16 7/8	42 1/8	26 5/8	43	47 3/4	18	13 1/4
67	8	27 3/8	48	22 5/8	24 3/8	28 7/8
33 5/8	27 1/2	21 3/4	24 1/4	24 5/8	20 1/4	33 5/8
49 3/4	23	10 1/8	33 1/2	87	28 1/8	16 3/4
35 1/4	25	31 1/4	13 1/8	17	28 1/2	64 5/8
56 3/4	27 3/8	21 1/8	24 1/4	33 1/8	24 1/8	43 1/4
75 1/4	34 1/4	12 7/8	12 3/8	45 3/4	67	13 3/4
22 3/4	49 1/8	29 7/8	58 3/8	44	29 3/8	17 1/2
41 1/4	99	6 1/4	24 1/2	26 3/8	42 7/8	34 7/8
14 5/8	30 5/8	9 7/8	61	106 1/4	33 3/8	30 3/4
9 3/8	25	70 3/4	100	50	32 1/2	17 1/2
36 1/2	16 5/8	5 7/8	36 1/4	17 7/8	93 3/4	21
26 5/8	37 7/8	30 1/4	40	10 5/8	61 5/8	21 1/4
26	23 3/4	11 3/8	18	15 1/4	13 5/8	57 5/8

classes. It is good practice to keep the classes of equal length. Thus, we can base our decision regarding how many to use on the range of the data—the difference between the largest and the smallest numbers. The highest price listed is 106 1/4 and the lowest is 5 7/8. Hence, we can conveniently choose the 11 classes having the *class limits* 0–9 7/8, 10–19 7/8, . . . , 100–109 7/8. Note that we did *not* choose the classes 0–10, 10–20, and so on. If we had, it would not have been clear in which class to include a stock closing, for example, at exactly $10. Note also that the class limits contain as many significant figures (the nearest eighth of a point) as the original data. In general, we choose classes that are *all of the same size* and that *do not over-lap*. Each closing price will fit neatly into one, and only one, of the 11 classes chosen.

The next step consists of tallying the 140 prices, by counting the number of prices in each class and putting a tally mark next to the class corresponding to each price (see Table 3).

TABLE 3 / *Tally of Number of Prices in Each Class*

Class Limits	Tally							Frequency
0–9 7/8	ᴺᴵ |							6
10–19 7/8	ᴺᴵ	ᴺᴵ	ᴺᴵ	ᴺᴵ	ᴺᴵ	ᴺᴵ	|	31
20–29 7/8	ᴺᴵ	ᴺᴵ	ᴺᴵ	ᴺᴵ	ᴺᴵ	ᴺᴵ	||||	34
30–39 7/8	ᴺᴵ	ᴺᴵ	ᴺᴵ	ᴺᴵ	|||			23
40–49 7/8	ᴺᴵ	ᴺᴵ	ᴺᴵ	||||				19
50–59 7/8	ᴺᴵ |							6
60–69 7/8	ᴺᴵ	ᴺᴵ						10
70–79 7/8	||||							4
80–89 7/8	||							2
90–99 7/8	|||							3
100–109 7/8	||							2
								140

Each observation in a given class has now lost some of its identity. We know, for example, that there were 6 stocks priced between 0 and 9 7/8, but we have lost their exact values. This leads to some difficulties when we wish to do further analysis with these data, but, as we shall see in Chapter 3, we can replace each datum by the class mark of the class in which it lies.

The *class mark* of any class is the arithmetic average of its class limits. Thus, the class mark of the second class is $(10 + 19\ 7/8)/2 = 14\ 15/16$. The 11 class marks in this frequency table are 4 15/16, 14 15/16, . . . ,

104 15/16. The common interval between any two successive class marks is called the *class interval*; in this example the common class interval equals 10. Note that we cannot talk about the class interval if the classes are not all of equal length; therefore, we should always use classes of equal length. We should also avoid open classes; for example, there may be a temptation to replace the last 4 classes by a single class (because they contain a total of only 11 observations) denoted by "$70 and over." If we succumb to this temptation, we shall be unable to do most of the statistical analysis of these data that are discussed in the next two chapters!

An alternate and often useful form of data presentation is the *cumulative frequency distribution* (see Table 4). A cumulative frequency distribution shows the

TABLE *4* / *Cumulative Frequency Distribution of 140 Closing Stock Prices*

Closing Price ($)	Number of Prices "Less Than"
10	6
20	37
30	71
40	94
50	113
60	119
70	129
80	133
90	135
100	138
110	140

number of observations that are less than the corresponding class limits. Such a table is easily constructed from the frequency table by successively adding (cumulating) the original frequencies. Thus, there are 6 prices *less than* $10 (not less than 9 7/8, because one or more of them could have been equal to 9 7/8); there are 37 prices less than $20, 71 less than $30, and so on.

Sometimes we may wish to compare two or more frequency distributions whose total frequencies are not equal. A convenient way to make such comparisons is to replace the frequencies by percentages of the total, that is, to convert the frequencies in the table to percentages. Table 5 shows the *percentage distribution*

TABLE 5 / *Distributions of 140 Closing Stock Prices*

PERCENTAGE DISTRIBUTION		CUMULATIVE DISTRIBUTION	
Class Limits	*Percent*	*Closing Price* ($)	*Percent Less Than*
0–9 7/8	4.3	10	4.3
10–19 7/8	22.2	20	26.5
20–29 7/8	24.3	30	50.8
30–39 7/8	16.4	40	67.2
40–49 7/8	13.6	50	80.8
50–59 7/8	4.3	60	85.1
60–69 7/8	7.1	70	92.2
70–79 7/8	2.9	80	95.1
80–89 7/8	1.4	90	96.5
90–99 7/8	2.1	100	98.6
100–109 7/8	1.4	110	100.0
	100.0		

and the *cumulative percentage distribution* corresponding to the frequency distribution of closing prices shown in Table 4.

Graphs of Frequency Distributions

Various important properties of frequency distributions become evident when we construct their graphs. To graph a frequency distribution, we locate the class marks on a horizontal scale or axis and center bars of equal width on these marks, each bar having a height proportional to the frequency (number of observations) in the class. The result is a bar chart, very similar to the bar charts in Figures 2 and 3. To emphasize that it represents a frequency distribution, we call such a graph a *frequency bar chart,* or *histogram.* The histogram of our 140 closing stock prices is shown in Figure 6. Note that we have added a "percent" scale on the right. Thus, this figure also can be regarded as the histogram of the percentage distribution of closing prices.

If we had succumbed to the temptation of combining the last 4 classes, *but had kept the last class closed* (class limits: 70–109 7/8), there would have been 11 prices in this combined class. The resulting histogram would have had a bar of height 11, whose base extends from 70 to 110. But the eye compares the areas of the bars, not their heights. Thus, we must interpret the *areas* of histograms as representing frequencies. Accordingly, because the combined class has 4 times the width of the other classes, we shall have to divide its frequency by 4, obtaining 2.75. The resulting histogram would then have a bar of height 2.75 (*not* 11) extending from 70 to 110.

Inspection of a histogram often brings out features that are hard to observe from the raw data themselves. One important feature concerns *shape*. Many distribu-

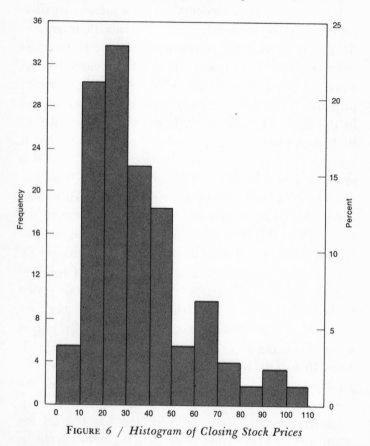

FIGURE *6 / Histogram of Closing Stock Prices*

tions have one or two high bars near the center, the heights of the other bars sloping off symmetrically on either side. Such a distribution is said to be *bell-shaped*. A very important bell-shaped distribution, called the normal distribution, will be introduced in Chapter 6. The opposite of a bell-shaped distribution is a so-called U-shaped distribution, in which the bars of smallest height are in the center. An example of data that might have a U-shaped distribution is the amount of cloud cover on a given day; in many climates days tend to be mostly overcast (nearly 100 percent cloud cover) or sunny (nearly 0 percent cloud cover).

The distribution of closing stock prices in Figure 6 has neither shape. It is not bell-shaped, because it is definitely unsymmetrical. Such a distribution is said to be *skewed*. A distribution has *positive skewness* if it slopes off more gradually to the right (has a right-hand "tail"), and it has *negative skewness* if it has a tail to the left. Data on prices, incomes, and many like kinds of economic statistics often have skewed distributions.

A class whose frequency is greater than that of its two adjacent neighbors is called a *modal class*. Its class mark is called a *mode* of the distribution. The distribution of closing stock prices has a single mode at 24 15/16. Distributions that have more than one mode (multimodal distributions) often describe data that come from two or more different "sources," such as populations, mechanisms, or underlying economic conditions.

The graph of a cumulative frequency distribution (see Figure 7) is called an *ogive*. We plot the cumulative frequencies (or percentages) on the vertical axis and the corresponding class limits on the horizontal axis. Ogives usually are S-shaped; the relative sizes of the two tails of the S are determined by the symmetry

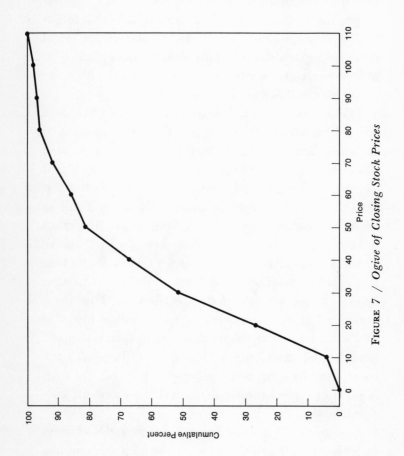

FIGURE 7 / *Ogive of Closing Stock Prices*

or lack of symmetry of the distribution. An examination of the ogive of Figure 7 quickly reveals some interesting facts about stock prices on the New York Stock Exchange. From our random sample of February 24, 1967, we infer that approximately half the common stocks were priced under $30. In fact, less than 2 percent were priced over $100.

We have seen that the application of a few simple tricks to long columns of data can result in simple graphs that immediately yield much of the important information contained in the data. In the next chapter, we shall discover how, by application of a few simple measures associated with frequency distributions, we can squeeze yet more information out of raw statistical data.

CHAPTER 3

The Average Game

Have you ever met the average man? He is 29.5 years old, has 2.17 children, has completed 10.6 years of school, earns $5,733 annually, and probably doesn't exist. These averages (based on 1960 census figures) are merely abstractions that attempt, somewhat imperfectly, to describe a large population of individuals.

The idea of an average becomes clearer when we consider a frequency distribution and ask, "What is its location?" To provide an answer, we want a representative number, one that is in some meaningful way *typical* of all the data comprising the distribution. Such a number, measuring the *central tendency* of a collection of statistical data, is called an *average*.

An average is a single number often used in place of an entire frequency distribution. Quite a trick! Obviously exclusive use of an average value, or use of the wrong average, can be grossly misleading. If you were told that the average annual income of a certain group of physicians is $15,000, would you be surprised to find that one of them earns $50,000? The answer depends not only on the average value but also on the shape of the distribution and the extent to which it is "spread out." In other words, it is important to know not only the central tendency or average of a set of data but also the extent to which the data depart from this average. In this chapter, we shall introduce the different kinds of averages that are most frequently used to describe the location of data, leaving to Chapter 4 our discussion of departures from the average.

What Kind of Average?

Frequency distributions have different shapes, and it is best not to use the same kind of average to describe the central tendency of each. The most commonly used averages are called the *mean,* the *median,* and the *mode.* When someone quotes an average value, he should state which kind of average he is talking about, because each has its own properties and their values can be quite different from one another.

The kind of average most commonly used is the *arithmetic mean,* or simply, the *mean.* It is a good general measure of central tendency because it locates the center of mass (or "center of gravity") of a frequency distribution. Suppose we imagine each data point to be a mass weighing one pound and arrange the data along a rigid rod so that each distance from one end of the rod equals the value of the corresponding data point. Now let us seek the point on the rod at which it just balances. The distance of this point from the reference end will exactly equal the mean of all the data points.

One may similarly interpret the mean of data that have been grouped into a frequency distribution. If we draw the histogram of the distribution on a piece of cardboard and cut it out, the point on the base line at which the histogram just balances is the mean of the distribution.

For a highly skewed distribution, however, the mean can be a poor measure of central tendency. The personnel manager of the XYZ Corporation, who recognized this fact, once advertised that in the past 12 months the average starting salary in his company was $12,000 per year. This figure attracted many trainee applicants, who later discovered that this average was the mean of five hirings; four were trainees hired at $6,000 and one was a vice-president hired at $36,000. A single observation, or only a few very unusual data points, can play havoc with the mean.

To avoid this problem, when dealing with skewed distributions we can use another kind of average called the *median*. The median divides the data into equal halves so that half the observations have values less than the median value and half have greater values. The median starting salary paid at the XYZ Corporation last year was $6,000; the mean was $12,000. What was the average starting salary? We can see now that this is a meaningless question—its answer depends strongly on what kind of average we are talking about.

As a general rule, income statistics have distributions that are positively skewed, reflecting the fact that many more persons have low incomes than the lucky few who have high incomes. Thus, it can be misleading to quote the "average" income of a group in terms of its mean value. (It will usually be too large to be representative.) A more reasonable practice is to give the median income.

Although the mean and the median are by far the most frequently used averages in economic statistics, there are a number of other averages that find special use. We shall briefly define the mode, the geometric mean, and the weighted mean.

Use of a mode is appropriate when the data are grouped into a frequency distribution. If any bar of the corresponding histogram is higher than its two immediately adjacent bars, the corresponding class is called a *modal* class. (The first or last class of a frequency table is a modal class if its single adjacent neighbor has a smaller frequency.) The *mode* itself is reasonably well approximated by the class mark of the corresponding modal class. Thus, a frequency distribution can have more than one mode, or, if all of its frequencies are equal, it can have no mode at all. For this reason, use of the mode as a measure of central tendency is usually restricted to cases in which there is exactly one mode.

If a frequency distribution is unimodal (has exactly one mode) and symmetric, then its mean, its median, and its mode will be identical. If a unimodal distribution is positively skewed, its mean will be greater than its median, which, in turn, will be greater than its mode. If such a distribution is negatively skewed, the order is reversed; the mode is greatest in value, followed by the median and then the mean.

The geometric mean is useful as a measure of central tendency for certain positively skewed distributions. Occasionally when dealing with economic data, taking the logarithm of each observation produces new data that are symmetrically distributed. Thus, the mean of the new data provides a better measure of central tendency than the mean of the original numbers. Converting the mean logarithm back to the original units by taking its antilogarithm produces the *geometric mean* of the original data. This kind of mean is less sensitive to "outliers" (a few unusually large values) than the arithmetic mean. (Incidentally, the procedure of taking the antilogarithm of the mean of the logarithms is mathematically equivalent to taking the n-th root of the product of the n observations.)

The *weighted mean* is often used when we have several groups of observations and the mean of each group is known. For example, if we have 3 groups, consisting of 5, 10, and 20 observations each, simple averaging of the 3 groups' means (adding them and dividing the resulting sum by 3) will not, in general, produce the mean of the combined group of 35 observations. Instead, we must *weight* each group mean by multiplying it by the number of observations in that group, add the resulting products, and divide by the sum of the weights. To illustrate, suppose the 3 group's means are respectively 9.8, 12.7, and 16.2. The simple mean of these three numbers is 12.9; the weighted mean is given by

$$\frac{(5 \times 9.8) + (10 \times 12.7) + (20 \times 16.2)}{5 + 10 + 20} = 14.3$$

Note the difference! Only the weighted mean correctly gives the overall mean of the 35 observations. We shall have more to say about weighted means when we apply them to index numbers in Chapter 8.

Calculating Averages—Raw Data

The following is the number of work stoppages during 1965 in 16 South Atlantic and South Central states:

16, 44, 32, 102, 25, 15, 61, 121, 99, 79, 70, 35, 31, 53, 44, 110

We shall use these numbers to illustrate the calculation of the mean, the median, and the geometric mean from data that have not been grouped.

The *mean* is simply the sum of the observations divided by the total number of observations. To express this as a general formula, suppose we refer to the value of the first observation by the symbol x_1, that of the second observation by x_2, the third by x_3, and so forth. If the total number of observations is symbolized by n, then the last observation will have the value x_n. Denoting the mean by the symbol $\bar{x}$, we then have

$$\bar{x} = \frac{1}{n} (x_1 + x_2 + x_3 + \ldots + x_n)$$

Application of this formula to the above data gives

$$\bar{x} = \frac{1}{16} (16 + 44 + 32 + \ldots + 110) = 58.6$$

for the mean number of work stoppages per state in this region during 1965.

To find the *median,* first we must rearrange the data in order of size. Choosing arbitrarily to order them from smallest to largest, we have

15, 16, 25, 31, 32, 35, 44, 44, 53, 61, 70, 79, 99, 102, 110, 121

For ungrouped data, the median is defined to be the "middlemost" observation. As we have 16 observations (an even number), there will be no middlemost one; instead there are two middle observations, namely, the eighth and ninth largest observations. Whenever n is even, as in this case, we define the median as the mean of the two middlemost observations. Thus, since the eighth largest value equals 44 and the ninth largest equals 53, the median is $(44 + 53)/2$, or 48.5. Note that the median (48.5) is considerably smaller in value than the mean (58.6). This is evidence that a frequency distribution of these data would be not symmetric but positively skewed; in other words, there were a few states in this group with an unusually large number of work stoppages in 1965.

To calculate the *geometric mean* of these 16 observations, we could follow one of two equivalent procedures. We could find the logarithm of each value, then calculate the mean of the 16 resulting logarithms, and finally take the antilogarithm of the result. Equivalently, we could multiply the 16 numbers together and find the sixteenth root of the resulting product. Using the first of these methods, we obtain the following 16 logarithms (to the base 10):

1.18, 1.64, 1.51, 2.01, 1.40, 1.77, 1.79, 2.08, 2.00, 1.90, 1.85, 1.54, 1.49, 1.72, 1.64, 2.04

Their mean is

$$\frac{1.18 + 1.64 + 1.51 + \ldots + 2.04}{16} = 1.723$$

Then, taking the antilogarithm of 1.723, we find that the geometric mean is 52.8.

Calculating the Mean—Grouped Data

When we must calculate descriptive measures for a large number of observations, we can save much time if we first group them into a frequency table and then calculate the mean and other measures to be described in the next chapter.

To illustrate, let us refer back to Table 3, a frequency table in which we grouped 140 stock prices into 11 classes. The class mark (average of the corresponding class limits) and corresponding frequency of each class is shown in Table 6. Suppose we are willing to accept the class mark of any given class as an approximation to the value of each observation in that class. Then, the sum of all the observations in a class is approximated by the class mark *times* the class frequency. For example, the first class has 6 observations, and its class mark is 4 15/16; thus, the sum of these 6 observations is approximated by 4 15/16 × 6, or 29 5/8.

If we add these products over all 11 classes, that is, calculate

$$(4\ 15/16 \times 6) + (14\ 15/16 \times 31) + (24\ 15/16 \times 34)$$
$$+ \ldots + (104\ 15/16 \times 2)$$

we get 4941.25, a close approximation to the sum of all 140 common stock prices. The mean price, then, is given by

$$\bar{x} = 4941.25/140 = 35.295$$

This method, although less tedious than adding all 140 prices and dividing by 140, is nonetheless time-consuming. A shortcut method, which allows this calculation to be made far more rapidly, involves the use of coding. Recognizing that the class marks are equally spaced (with the common class interval $C = 10$), we can replace them by any convenient set of *equally spaced* small whole numbers. For greatest ease in calculations, we shall replace the class mark of the middle class by *zero,* counting in steps of size 1 in either direction. Since our coded values must proceed from smaller to larger just as the class marks do, we must use negative numbers above the zero, and positive numbers below (see the fourth column in Table 6, labeled u).

Now we proceed to find the mean of the u-values in exactly the same way that we found the mean of the x-values. First, we form a column labeled uf, giving the product of each u-value and the corresponding frequency. Then we sum these products, obtaining -275. Finally, the mean of the u-values is calculated to be $-275/140 = -1.9643$.

The only question that remains to be answered is how we go from the mean of the u-values to the mean of the x-values? To answer this question, we reason as follows. Let x_0 represent the class mark that we arbitrarily chose to replace with $u = 0$. In this case, $x_0 = 54\ 15/16$.

TABLE 6 / *Computation of the Mean—Grouped Data*

Class i	Class Mark x	Frequency f	u	uf
1	4 15/16	6	−5	−30
2	14 15/16	31	−4	−124
3	24 15/16	34	−3	−102
4	34 15/16	23	−2	−46
5	44 15/16	19	−1	−19
6	54 15/16	6	0	0
7	64 15/16	10	1	10
8	74 15/16	4	2	8
9	84 15/16	2	3	6
10	94 15/16	3	4	12
11	104 15/16	2	5	10
		140		−275

$$\bar{u} = \frac{-275}{140} = -1.9643$$

$$\bar{x} = 54.9375 - (10 \times 1.9643) = 35.295$$

By adding or subtracting steps of 10 units to x_0, we get any of the other class marks in x. For example, the x-value corresponding to $u = 3$ is obtained by *adding* 3 steps of 10 units each to 54 15/16, for a total of 84 15/16. To go in the other direction, the x-value corresponding to $u = -2$ is obtained by *subtracting* two steps of 10 units each from 54 15/16, for a net result of 34 15/16. In general, if C is the class interval, the relationship linking x to the corresponding coded value u is given by

$$x = x_0 + C u$$

(Try the values $x_0 = 54$ 15/16, $C = 10$, and $u = -4$ in this formula and see that you get $x = 14$ 15/16, the class mark opposite the u-value −4 in Table 6.)

One more step and we have a simple formula relating the mean of the x-values to the mean of the u-values. It can be shown that *the mean of the* x-*values equals* x_0 *plus the product of the class interval and the mean of the* u-*values,* or

$$\bar{x} = x_0 + C\,\bar{u}$$

In our example $\bar{u} = -1.9643$, the class interval is 10, and $x_0 = 54\ 15/16 = 54.9375$. Thus,

$$\bar{x} = 54.9375 - (10 \times 1.9643) = 35.295$$

Note that this result agrees exactly with the mean of $\bar{x}$ calculated directly on page 35. (The reader who has the time might wish to calculate the mean price directly from the 140 observations listed on page 17 to see how close this value comes to 35.295.)

Summarizing, we can drastically reduce the time required to calculate the mean of a large number of observations by grouping and then coding the resulting class marks. Regardless of where we locate $u = 0$, if we use u-values of -1, -2, -3, and so on, as we go upward from zero in the table, and 1, 2, 3, and so on, as we go downward from zero, the method just described will give the correct result.

CHAPTER 4

Departures From the Average

An investor doing research into the past earnings of
two companies finds that each has returned a mean
profit of 10 percent on investment during the last 20
years. Does this mean that each is an equally good
candidate for investment? Let us explore the question
further by examining the pattern of returns for each
over the past 20 years. In Figure 8, histograms, showing
the distribution of earnings for each company, reveal an
interesting and important difference. An investment in
the AAA Corporation during any one of the last 20
years would never have produced a loss; neither would
it have produced a gain in excess of 20 percent. On the
other hand, during 3 of the last 20 years the ZZZ Corporation lost money. (This is counterbalanced by the
fact that during 3 of these years it earned in excess of
20 percent.)

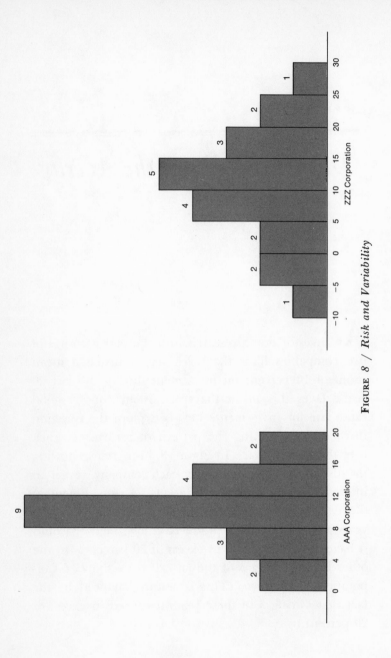

FIGURE 8 / *Risk and Variability*

If the pattern of earnings for each company as shown in these histograms should repeat over the next several years, we could expect a return of 10 percent—on the average—regardless of which company we chose. However, if our choice is to invest in the AAA Corporation we are virtually assured that there will be no loss. In fact, the odds strongly favor a return of at least 4 percent. An investment in the ZZZ Corporation, however, could well result in a return of less than 4 percent next year, perhaps even a loss. Of course, there is also the chance that such an investment might bring an excess of 20 percent.

The two distributions shown in Figure 8 have the same mean, but they differ considerably in their "spread." The earnings of the AAA Corporation during the past 20 years were far less *variable* than the earnings of the ZZZ Corporation. Based on this information alone, the ZZZ Corporation represents a riskier investment than the AAA Corporation. More generally, the concept of variability plays an important role in all of statistics.

Measurement of Variability

Perhaps the simplest and most straightforward way to measure the variability of economic data is to ask, "What is the range of the data?" The *range* is simply the difference between the largest and the smallest observation. Although it is easy to calculate and to interpret, it suffers from the disadvantage that it is extremely sensitive to unusually large or unusually small observations. A single outlying observation (which may be spurious) can have an enormous effect on the range.

A more stable measure of variability can be based on the extent to which the observations cluster about the mean. For each observation we can ask, "How far is it from the mean?" The *deviation* of an observation from its mean is defined as the value of that observation, minus the mean value. At first it would seem that all we have to do to construct a good measure of variability is to find the average value of these deviations from the mean. Unfortunately, as can be proved mathematically, *the sum of all the deviations from the mean always equals zero*. Intuition tells us that this should be true, because observations greater than the mean will have a positive deviation and observations less than the mean will have a negative deviation, and when they are added together, the positive deviations will cancel the negative deviations.

Fortunately, we can get out of this difficulty without dropping the intuitively appealing idea of deviations from the mean. Perhaps the simplest way around the problem is to drop the minus sign, averaging all departures from the mean as if they were positive. The measure of variability that results is called the *mean deviation*.

However, a second method of handling the signed deviations has better mathematical and statistical properties. Instead of merely dropping the minus signs, we can square each of the deviations from the mean, calculating the mean of these squared deviations. In finding this mean we must be careful about choosing the divisor. If we have 10 observations, for example, we can correspondingly calculate 10 deviations from the mean of these observations. Because we know that these 10 deviations will add to zero, once 9 of them have been calculated, the tenth is then *predetermined*. Surprising as it may seem, therefore, there are really only 9 *independent* deviations from the mean, and we should divide the sum of the squares of the 10 calculated deviations by 9 instead of by 10!

This thinking leads to the measure of variation called the *variance*. To illustrate its definition, suppose we calculate the variance of the 20 annual returns on investment obtained by the AAA Corporation, which are graphed in Figure 8. The actual values of these 20 percentages are:

13, 9, 10, 3, 13, 14, 9, 10, 17, 11, 6, 7, 10, 3, 5, 9, 10, 18, 15, 8

and you can easily verify that the mean of these 20 observations is 10 percent. The deviation of the first observation (13) from the mean is $13 - 10 = 3$, the deviation of the second observation (9) from the mean is $9 - 10 = -1$, and so forth. The 20 deviations from the mean are as follows:

3, −1, 0, −7, 3, 4, −1, 0, 7, 1, −4, −3, 0, −7, −5, −1, 0, 8, 5, −2

You can easily check to see that the sum of these 20 deviations is, indeed, equal to zero. Squaring these deviations, we get

9, 1, 0, 49, 9, 16, 1, 0, 49, 1, 16, 9, 0, 49, 25, 1, 0, 64, 25, 4

These are the 20 squared deviations whose mean we are

to calculate in obtaining the variance. Since the first 19 determine the 20th (their sum is zero), in calculating the variance we divide by 19, and not by 20. The result is

$$S^2 = \frac{9 + 1 + 0 + 49 + \ldots + 25 + 4}{19} = \frac{328}{19} = 17.3$$

An *alternative method* of calculating the variance of ungrouped data makes the computation much easier, especially if a desk calculator is used. With this formula it is not necessary first to compute the mean, then to subtract the mean from each observation, then to square and add the resulting deviations, and finally to divide by $n - 1$. Instead, we go through the observations only once, and with a desk calculator we can find their sum and the sum of their squares in this one operation. With one more operation on a desk calculator, we can multiply the *sum of the squares* by n (the number of observations) and subtract the *square of the sum*. We now need only to divide by the product of n and $(n - 1)$ to complete the calculation. (The reader who has access to a desk calculator is urged to check this formula by obtaining the result 17.3 for the variance of the 20 returns given on page 43.)

Use of this *computing formula* for the variance has another advantage, too. As you know, serious round-off errors can occur whenever we do calculations and, in particular, whenever we divide. Use of the *defining formula* for calculating the variance involves first a division to calculate the mean, and then a series of 20 successive subtractions to obtain the deviations from the mean. Any round-off error in calculating the mean will be reflected in each of the deviations. Note, however, that when we use the computing formula for calculating the variance, we have only one subtraction and only one division. Furthermore, these two calculations producing round-off errors are postponed until the very end, where they will do the least harm.

The original observations from which we calculated this variance were in units of percentage return. Since we squared the deviations, however, the variance no longer has the same units as the original observations. To compensate, we can now take the *square root of the variance* to obtain $\sqrt{17.3} = 4.2$. The resulting measure is called the *standard deviation.*

The sum of the 20 deviations themselves, after dropping the minus signs, is 62. Thus, the mean deviation equals 3.1, and it is smaller than the standard deviation, 4.2. In general, this will always be true; by squaring, when we calculate the standard deviation—even though we later take the square root—we give more relative weight to observations very far from the mean.

Calculating Standard Deviations From Grouped Data

Many poor decisions are made because we tend to base them on average values only, without bothering to ask, "How big are the departures from this average?" It is not too hard to understand the reason for this tendency to ignore variability. First, the foregoing description shows that calculation of a standard deviation is a somewhat tedious process. Second, once the standard deviation is calculated, many of us have difficulty interpreting it. The purpose of this section is to show that the calculation of the standard deviation can be made far less tedious by grouping the data and using coded values. In the next section, we hope to give the reader some insight into how one can interpret the standard deviation, and base rational decisions upon its value.

To calculate the standard deviation from grouped data, we have only to add one more column to Table 6. That table, with the extra column added, is repro-

TABLE 7 / *Computation of the Standard Deviation—Grouped Data*

Class i	Class Mark x	Frequency f	u	uf	u²f
1	4 15/16	6	−5	−30	150
2	14 15/16	31	−4	−124	496
3	24 15/16	34	−3	−102	306
4	34 15/16	23	−2	−46	92
5	44 15/16	19	−1	−19	19
6	54 15/16	6	0	0	0
7	64 15/16	10	1	10	10
8	74 15/16	4	2	8	16
9	84 15/16	2	3	6	18
10	94 15/16	3	4	12	48
11	104 15/16	2	5	10	50
		140		−275	1205

$$S_u^2 = \frac{(140 \times 1205) - (-275)^2}{140 \times 139}$$

$$= \frac{168,700 - 75,625}{19,460} = 4.78$$

$$S_x^2 = 10^2 \times 4.78 = 478$$

$$S_x = 21.9$$

duced here as Table 7. The new column (the last column in Table 7) is obtained by multiplying each frequency by the *square* of the corresponding u-value, and the sum of the 11 numbers in this column is 1205.

The number 1205, obtained by adding the u^2f column, is a close approximation to the sum of the squares of all 140 u-values. We shall use the computing formula to produce the variance of the u-values. First, we multiply 1205 by 140. Then we subtract the square of the sum of the u-values, which sum we previously calculated to be −275. Finally we divide the result by 140×139, or 19,460. The calculations are shown underneath Table 7, and we obtain 4.78 for the variance of the u-values.

Analogous to what we did when we calculated the mean in Chapter 3, we must now find a way to go from the variance of the u-values to the variance of the x-values. From our previous discussion, we already know that

$$x = x_0 + Cu$$

that is, each x-value equals a constant (x_0) plus the class interval (C) times the corresponding u-value. Thus, we must ask, "What happens to the variance of a set of numbers if we add a constant to each number, and if we multiply each number by a constant?" First, let us add the same constant to each one of the set of observations and see what happens. Picturing the histogram of these observations in our mind's eye, we can see that adding a constant simply shifts the entire diagram to the right or to the left by an amount equal to the value of the constant. Thus, it will shift the mean, but it will not change the *shape* of the histogram. In other words, adding a constant will not change the "spread" of the observations, and therefore it will not change the variance.

Multiplication by a fixed constant produces a different result. If we multiply each observation by some number, clearly the result will be to multiply the mean by the same number. Consequently, it follows that each deviation will be multiplied by this constant, and each *squared* deviation will be multiplied by the *square* of this constant. Thus, the relationship between the variance of the u-values and the variance of the x-values is given by

$$S_x{}^2 = C^2 S_u{}^2$$

Taking the square root of each side, we see that the standard deviation of the x-values is simply the class interval, C, times the standard deviation of the u-values, or

$$S_x = C S_u$$

Because we chose a class interval of $C = 10$ to group these 140 stock prices, and because the variance of the u-values is 4.78, the variance of the x-values will equal 100 times 4.78, or 478. Thus, the standard deviation of the 140 stock prices is $\sqrt{478} = 21.9$, expressed as a decimal.

Interpreting the Standard Deviation

Most economic statistics are given in terms of some kind of average. We can readily imagine a situation in which a businessman is quite interested in an average value, but can we imagine anyone getting excited over a standard deviation? Yet it is remarkable how much knowledge of *both* the mean and the standard deviation can reveal about the source of the observations. *Together, the mean and the standard deviation place very definite limits on the values that can be assumed by the observations.*

To understand more fully the meaning of this last statement, let us measure each observed value in *standard units*. That is, let us ask, "How many standard deviations away from the mean does this observation lie?" If an observation has the value x, and the mean of the data from which it was taken is $\bar{x}$, then the quantity $x - \bar{x}$ measures the distance (or, as we have called it, the deviation) of this observation from the mean. If the standard deviation is S, the quantity

$$\frac{x - \bar{x}}{S}$$

measures the number of standard deviations by which x departs from $\bar{x}$. For example, because the mean of our 140 stock prices is 35.3 and the standard deviation is 21.9, a stock valued at \$57.2 lies one standard deviation above the mean, because

$$\frac{57.2 - 35.3}{21.9} = 1$$

How far can an observation be from its mean? Amazingly, an observation is rarely more than a few standard deviations on either side of the mean of the distribution from which that observation was obtained. In fact, a

famous mathematician, P. L. Chebychev, was able to
calculate the odds against an observation having a value
more than plus or minus a given number of standard
units.

Chebychev proved by mathematical arguments that
the odds are at least 3 to 1 against the value of an observation (in standard units) being more than $+2$ or less
than -2. This means that the chances are quite small
indeed that an observation will be more than two standard deviations on either side of the mean. In Table
8 we show the minimum odds against the value of an

TABLE 8 / *Odds Against Deviation From the Mean*

Number of Standard Units	Minimum Odds Against Exceeding This Value	Approximate Odds for a Normal Distribution
2	3–1	21–1
3	8–1	369–1
4	15–1	15,800–1
5	24–1	1,740,000–1

observation (in standard units) deviating from the mean
by more than the stated number of standard units.

The remarkable thing about this result is that it does
not depend on the shape of the distribution. Whether
the distribution is symmetric or skewed, bell-shaped or
U-shaped, these results are still correct. As these are
minimum odds, they can be exceeded for certain distributions. For example, if we know that the observations
come from a normal distribution (to be discussed in
detail in Chapter 6), the odds against exceeding these
values are much greater, as shown in the third column of
the table.

Let us apply these odds to the earnings data given on page 43. Based on a sample of earnings over the past 20 years, we have calculated that the mean percentage return for the AAA Corporation is 10 percent, and the standard deviation is 4.2 percent. Assuming that these statistics continue to hold over the next several years, what can we say about the earnings of this company for the next year? Chebychev tells us that the odds are at least 3 to 1 against earnings of more than two standard deviations on either side of the mean. In other words, it is at least a 3 to 1 gamble that the earnings will not exceed 18.4 percent or be less than 1.6 percent. This is a big spread, but at least it does not include a loss (negative earnings). If we could further assume that these earnings were distributed according to the normal distribution, the corresponding odds would go up to 21 to 1.

The corresponding standard deviation for the ZZZ Corporation is considerably larger. In fact, by using the method for calculating standard deviations from grouped data that was discussed in the preceding section, it can be calculated that the standard deviation is 8.7 for the ZZZ Corporation. Thus, for at least 3 to 1 odds we would have to gamble that the earnings would be less than − 7.4 percent or greater than 27.4 percent. This spread is so large that we are, in effect, saying that predictions about next year's earnings for the ZZZ Corporation are extremely tenuous. In other words, when faced with a large standard deviation, knowledge of the mean value contributes little to our ability to predict the value of a future data point.

Here is perhaps a more poignant example of the effect of the standard deviation on our ability to predict. We shall see in Chapter 6 that, for normally distributed data, there is only about 1 chance in 6 that an observation will assume a value less than 1 standard deviation below the mean. Thus, it is a fairly good gamble to assume that an investment in the AAA Corporation will not yield less than 10 − 4.2, or 5.8 percent next year. In other words, the odds of earning *at least* 5.8 percent are approximately 5 to 1 on the assumption that these data come from a normal distribution. The same gamble (5 to 1) with an investment in the ZZZ Corporation, however, will guarantee only that the return will exceed 1.3 percent.

What can we say about the stock market, based on these criteria? As we shall see in Chapter 6, the normal distribution is symmetric and bell-shaped. We have already made the observation that the distribution of the 140 common-stock prices is definitely skewed to the right. Thus, it would be unrealistic to assume that these prices come from a normal distribution. Without further characterizing the distribution of stock prices on the New York Stock Exchange, the best we could then do would be to use the minimum odds given by Chebychev. Since the mean price in our earlier example was $35.3 and the standard deviation was $21.9, about all we can be assured of (with minimum odds of 3 to 1) is that a stock chosen at random from this list would have been valued at less than $79.1.

The moral of the story is simply this: When faced with a large standard deviation, don't bet too heavily on the mean.

CHAPTER 5

Taking a Chance

Virtually every business decision involves some element of risk. In deciding whether or not to invest in a certain business venture, we are concerned with the chance that the venture will succeed. In forecasting the economy, we are interested in knowing the probability that our forecast may be off by a certain amount. In pricing a product or a service so as to maximize expected profit, we must have some information about the proportion of potential customers who will purchase the product at each possible price.

Because the outcome of almost any decision cannot be predicted with certainty, it is important that we understand measures of uncertainty, or probabilities. Generally speaking, decision-making in the face of uncertainty involves the use of a collection of information germane to the decision at hand in order to predict the consequences of any one of a set of possible decisions.

In statistical inference, for example, the collection of information may be the results of a random sample, and we may wish to decide whether or not the mean of the population from which the sample was selected is greater than, or less than, a certain number. Regardless of which decision we make, there is a chance that we will be wrong. A general problem of statistical inference is to select a decision-making procedure that, in some way, reduces the chances of such errors to a minimum. We shall have more to say about the specific applications of probabilities to problems of statistical inference in Chapter 7.

What Are Probabilities?

Suppose we think of an "experiment" as very broadly any process or procedure that results in a definable collection of possible outcomes. For example, the toss of a coin can be regarded as an experiment, and its possible outcomes are "heads" and "tails." A question-naire sent to banks to determine the average monthly cost of electronic data processing also can be regarded as an experiment, and its possible outcomes (expressed to the nearest dollar) can be regarded as the set of integers 0, 1, 2, and so forth.

Before performing an experiment, we cannot know with certainty which outcomes will result. If we have performed the experiment often enough in the past, however, we would have observed that some of the outcomes occur more frequently than others. In other words, the next experimental observation may be "more likely" to take on one value than another. A number associated with an outcome of an experiment, which expresses the frequency with which that outcome will occur relative to the other possible outcomes, is called a *probability*.

Given a set of logically possible outcomes of an experiment, how does one go about assigning to each outcome these mysterious numbers called "probabilities"? We have already hinted at one method, called the method of *relative frequencies*. To apply this method similar experiments must have been performed many times in the past. If a record of the outcomes has been kept, we can count the number of times that each different outcome has occurred. If, for a given outcome, we divide its frequency of occurrence by the total number of trials of the experiment, we obtain its relative frequency of occurrence. This number can be used as an estimate of the probability of that outcome. Of course, the larger the number of trials upon which this estimate is based, the closer the relative frequency will be to the "true" probability.

This method of assigning probabilities to outcomes leads to a tentative definition of probability. Essentially, this definition says that the probability of an outcome is its relative frequency *in the long run*. In other words, probabilities are merely relative frequencies in which the total number of experiments (or trials) is indefinitely large. Although there are certain philosophical difficulties with this definition, it nonetheless leads to a good intuitive description of probabilities, as well as to a very practical method for evaluating them in many instances.

As an illustration of the method of relative frequencies, suppose we are in the business of manufacturing diesel engines, and we are interested in predicting the number of monthly orders for these engines. Utilizing monthly sales records over the past 10 years, we could construct a table like Table 9.

TABLE *9 / Orders of Diesel Engines per Month*

Number of orders	0	1	2	3	4	5	6	7	8	9	10	Total
Frequency	3	5	9	17	17	25	22	12	7	2	1	120
Relative frequency	.025	.042	.075	.142	.142	.208	.183	.100	.058	.017	.008	1.000

From this table we would estimate that the probability of 6 orders in a given month is 0.183 (that is, nearly 1 month in 5 will produce orders for 6 engines), that the probability of no orders is 0.025 (that is, only in 1 month in 40 will no orders arrive), and that the probability of more than 10 orders is zero. These estimates all are based on the assumption that future orders will come in as in the past. If sales have been changing steadily so that there is an upward trend in the number of orders, or if there is a seasonal or cyclical variation in the number of orders, these estimates would require corresponding adjustment.

Assignment of probabilities to a collection of outcomes, derived by the method of relative frequencies, has two major drawbacks. First, the resulting probabilities are approximations because the number of available trials always is limited. Second, even these approximations are suspect unless the experiment that produced the relative frequencies was identical in every respect to the experiment whose outcomes are to be predicted. Unfortunately, the sales picture for diesel engines will never be the same tomorrow as it was yesterday; there has never existed in the past exactly the same business venture in which we are now contemplating investment; the state of economy, in all its complexity, has never been exactly what it is today. Thus, although relative frequencies are extremely useful for obtaining probabilities in certain fields—especially engineering and the physical sciences, where more exact repetitions of experimental conditions are possible—their usefulness is more limited in business and economic applications.

A second important and frequently used method of obtaining probabilities consists simply in *assuming* their values. This method may not be as arbitrary or impractical as at first it may seem. For example, given a coin minted by the U.S. Treasury, few of us would argue with the assumption that the probability is one-half (or one out of two) that it will come up "heads" when tossed. This is purely an assumption, based on the physical construction of the coin and the method used in tossing it. An unbalanced coin or an "unfair" method of tossing it can void this assumption.

As another example, if a deck of 52 playing cards has been thoroughly shuffled, few of us would argue with the conclusion that the probability of cutting a spade is one-fourth. We are willing to make this assumption because it appears to be the only one consistent with our understanding of what takes place when a card is thus selected from an "honest" deck.

In calculating the probability that a coin would come up "heads" or in calculating the chance of obtaining a spade when drawing from a thoroughly shuffled deck of cards, we tacitly assumed that all possible outcomes could be assigned equal probability weights. This assumption, called the assumption of *equal likelihood,* sometimes is used to give a "definition" of probability. According to this definition, if an experiment has n "equally likely" outcomes among which s are successes, then the probability of a success is "defined" as s/n. Although this statement expresses an idea useful in the calculation of probabilities, it fails as a rigorous definition of probability because it is circular, that is, it uses the term "equally likely" in the definition of the word "probability."

There are many situations in which we are tempted to give all possible outcomes' the same probability weight. (In games of chance, great pains are taken to see that this assumption is reasonably well satisfied.) When we face the realities of economics, however, we find that the assumption of "equally distributed ignorance" seldom pays off. The experienced businessman usually can make a more intelligent judgment about the relative likelihood of various possible outcomes.

Situations sometimes arise in the course of making business decisions in which there does not exist a large enough body of previous experience upon which to base a relative-frequency estimate of a required probability, or for which the underlying mechanisms are not sufficiently understood to make possible a reasonable assumption about a required probability. In such situations the businessman may "feel in his bones" that certain outcomes may be more likely than certain others. It is very difficult for him to express these feelings numerically, in the form of probabilities. But, if he is to calculate the consequences of possible decisions, he may be called upon to do so. Such probabilities, based on expert opinion or judgment, are sometimes called *subjective probabilities*.

Modern methods of statistical inference that are particularly suitable to business decisions require us to estimate the probabilities of certain outcomes before making any observations. In estimating *prior* probabilities, sometimes we are forced to express our subjective feelings in the form of numbers; in other words, sometimes we *must* use subjective probabilities.

How Do Probabilities Behave?

As we have seen, a probability is a number expressing the relative likelihood of obtaining a given outcome of an "experiment." To describe the behavior of probabilities let us refer to the collection of all possible outcomes of the experiment under consideration by the term *sample space,* and denote it by the letter S. A particular outcome will be denoted by another letter such as A or B. We shall use the symbol $P(A)$ to stand for the probability that we obtain the outcome A.

Since a probability is interpretable as a relative frequency, it can never be negative nor can it exceed the value 1 (corresponding to 100 percent). Also, because each possible outcome belongs to the sample space (by definition), the probability of the sample space must equal 1. Expressing these ideas more formally, we state two fundamental laws of probability.

Axiom 1 For any event, A, in the sample space, S, $P(A)$ is a number lying between 0 and 1.

Axiom 2 $$P(S) = 1$$

The word *event* in Axiom 1 simply refers to any collection of outcomes of an experiment. By definition, whatever outcome occurs must belong to S, the sample space. Thus, Axiom 2 expresses the idea that the probability of a *logically certain event* is 1.

Suppose we now consider two events in S; let us call them A and B. For example, S might refer to the collection of the 52 possible outcomes when a card is drawn from a thoroughly shuffled deck. The event A might refer to the collection of 13 outcomes corresponding to "a spade is drawn"; the event B might refer to the collection of the 13 outcomes corresponding to "a heart is drawn." If the deck has been thoroughly shuffled, it is reasonable to suppose that each outcome in S has the same probability as each other outcome in S. In other words, the probability of any outcome equals 1/52.

How can we use this information to find the probability that a spade is drawn? Because there are 13 individual outcomes corresponding to the event that a spade is chosen, and because each one has the probability 1/52, it would seem logical that the probability of the event comprising these 13 outcomes equals 13/52, or 1/4. To obtain this result we simply added the probabilities of the 13 individual outcomes comprising the event "a spade is drawn."

The idea that we can add the probabilities of the individual outcomes to obtain the probability of an event, a collection of outcomes, can be further exploited. Suppose that A and B are *disjoint* events, that is, they contain no outcome in common. (In other words, to use less formal language, these events cannot both happen at the same time.) Now if one of the outcomes making up the event A should occur or if one of the outcomes making up the event B should occur, then we say that the event A *or* B has occurred.

The event A *or* B is an example of a *compound* event, that is, a new event that is the result of combining two *simple* events. In connection with this kind of compound event we can state

Axiom 3 (*Special Law of Addition*). If A and B are disjoint events in S, then

$$P(A \text{ or } B) = P(A) + P(B)$$

In other words, we can find the probability that one or the other of two disjoint events will occur simply by adding the probabilities of the individual events. For example, the probability of drawing a spade *or* a heart from a well-shuffled deck is $1/4 + 1/4$, or $1/2$.

These three simple axioms can enable us to obtain a large number of useful and important rules concerning the behavior of probabilities. We probably have made conscious or unconscious use of most of these rules at one time or another without realizing that they are mathematical theorems that can be proved rigorously, using only the three basic axioms already presented.

Rule 1 $P(A$ will not occur$) = 1 - P(A)$

Thus, for example, if the probability is 0.6 (60 percent) that a certain business venture will succeed, then the probability is 0.4 (40 percent) that it will fail. As an immediate consequence of Rule 1, we obtain

Rule 2 $P(S$ will not occur$) = 0$

Since S refers to the collection of all possible outcomes, the event "S will not occur" is a logically impossible event. This rule simply states that the probability of a *logically impossible event* is zero.

Axiom 3 told us that we could add the probabilities of disjoint events to find the probability that either one or the other will occur. It did not tell us, however, what to do if the two events were not disjoint, that is, if they contained certain outcomes in common. If the two events A and B contain certain outcomes in common, there will be one or more outcomes in the compound event A *and* B. If we simply add $P(A)$ and $P(B)$, as indicated by Axiom 3, we will count such outcomes twice; but we can correct the overcount by subtracting $P(A$ *and* $B)$. Expressing this idea formally, we have

Rule 3 (General Law of Addition).

$$P(A \text{ } or \text{ } B) = P(A) + P(B) - P(A \text{ } and \text{ } B)$$

To illustrate Rule 3, let us again suppose that A is

the event that consists in drawing a spade from a well-shuffled deck of 52 playing cards, but this time we shall let *B* denote the event that consists in drawing an ace. Note that these two events overlap, the overlap consisting of a single outcome, namely, the ace of spades. The compound event *A or B* is the event that consists in drawing either a spade or an ace. According to the general law of addition (Rule 3) the probability of this event equals the probability of *A* plus the probability of *B*, *minus* the probability of both *A and B*. The subtraction of $P(A \text{ and } B)$ is necessary to avoid counting this event twice, as it occurs in both *A* and *B*.

Again assuming equal likelihood, the probability of *A* equals 13/52 or 1/4, and the probability of *B* equals 4/52 or 1/13. As there is only one outcome in the compound event *A and B* (the ace of spades), the probability of this event is 1/52. Thus, we obtain

$$P(A \text{ or } B) = P(A) + P(B) - P(A \text{ and } B)$$
$$= 1/4 + 1/13 - 1/52 = 4/13$$

Expressed verbally, the probability that we draw an ace *or* a spade is 4/13.

Now, suppose we want to find the probability that the card selected is an ace, *given that it was a spade*. Here we are concerned with a reduced sample space consisting of the 13 spades only; it contains 13 cards, one of which is an ace. Again assuming equal likelihood, we obtain the probability of drawing an ace, *given that we drew a spade,* to be 1/13. Using the symbol $P(B \mid A)$ to denote this probability, we observe that

$P(B \mid A) = 1/13$. Recalling that $P(B)$ equals $4/52$, or $1/13$, we note that in this case $P(B \mid A) = P(B)$.

The probability $P(B \mid A)$ is called the *conditional probability of* B *given* A, and in the example given it had the same value as $P(B)$, the *unconditional* probability of B. For an example in which $P(B \mid A)$ does not equal $P(B)$, consider the following. Two balls are drawn from a bowl containing one white ball and two red balls. The first ball is *not replaced* before drawing the second ball. Let A represent the event that a white ball is chosen by the first draw, and let B denote the event that a red ball is chosen by the second draw. To find the conditional probability $P(B \mid A)$, we reason as follows. If a white ball is drawn on the first trial, then before drawing the second ball the bowl consists of no white balls and two red balls. Thus, the probability of drawing a red ball on the second trial, *given that a white ball was drawn on the first trial,* equals 1. In other words, on the condition that we drew a white ball the first time, it is certain that we would have gotten a red ball on the second draw. If we remove this condition, however, it is clearly not certain that we would have drawn a red ball on the second try. For example, we might have drawn a red ball on the first try, and then the white ball could have been drawn on the second try.

Note that, had we *replaced* the first ball before drawing the second ball, we would have obtained $P(B \mid A) = 2/3$, because there still would be three balls remaining for the second draw, two of which are red and one of which is white. This agrees with the *unconditional probability* of drawing a red ball, $P(B)$; in other words, $P(B \mid A) = P(B)$ when the first ball drawn is replaced. This result is intuitively evident because the probability of drawing a red ball on the second try no longer depends on the result of the first try. Thus, we say that A and B are *independent events*. In general, whenever $P(A \mid B) = P(A)$ or $P(B \mid A) = P(B)$, we say that A and B are independent events.

If A and B are independent events, we can state the following rule for finding the probability of the compound event A *and* B.

Rule 4 (Special Law of Multiplication—Independent Events).

$$P(A \text{ and } B) = P(A)P(B)$$

If A and B are not independent, however, we must use conditional probabilities to find the probability of A *and* B, as follows.

Rule 5 (General Law of Multiplication).

$$P(A \text{ and } B) = P(A)P(B \mid A)$$
$$= P(B)P(A \mid B)$$

As a further illustration of the laws of addition and multiplication for probabilities, let us consider the following example. Suppose that the probability of a missile hitting its target on a given firing is 0.70. What is the probability that at least one missile will hit the target if two are launched? Suppose we let A stand for the event that the first missile hits the target and let B stand for the event that the second missile hits it. Because $P(A) = P(B) = 0.70$, then the probability of A *or* B is given by Rule 3 to be

$$P(A \ or \ B) = P(A) + P(B) - P(A \ and \ B)$$
$$= 0.70 + 0.70 - P(A \ and \ B)$$

To evaluate $P(A \ and \ B)$, the probability that both shots hit the target, we would have to know whether A and B are independent events. For the moment, let us assume that they are; that is, let us assume that the accuracy of the second missile does not depend upon whether the first missile hits its target. Then we can use Rule 4 to obtain

$$P(A \ and \ B) = P(A)P(B)$$
$$= (0.70)(0.70) = 0.49$$

Thus, the probability that either missile hits the target equals

$$0.70 + 0.70 - 0.49 = 0.91$$

This result shows that the probability of hitting the target with *at least one missile* increases from 0.70 when one missile is fired at the target to 0.91 when two missiles are fired, an increase in the probability of only 0.21, not 0.70. Note that we would have obtained the absurd result $P(A \ or \ B) = 1.40$ had we forgotten to subtract $P(A \ and \ B)$.

Prior Probabilities and the Rule of Bayes

The general law of multiplication is useful in solving many problems in which the ultimate outcome of an experiment depends on the outcomes of several intermediate stages. To illustrate, suppose we are concerned with the probability that a certain order will arrive on time. When the order was placed for this shipment, it could have been handled in one of two ways. If the items requested were available in the supplier's local warehouse, they would have been shipped directly with little loss of time. On the other hand, if these items had to be back-ordered, there is a good chance that the shipment would have arrived late.

From past experience with these kinds of orders, we have observed that the likelihood is 0.75 that the shipment could have been delivered directly from the warehouse, and therefore the chances are 0.25 that it had to be back-ordered. In other words,

$$P(W) = 0.75 \text{ and } P(B) = 0.25$$

where W represents the event that the order could be shipped directly from the warehouse, and B represents the event that it had to be back-ordered. Prior experience also shows that if the order has been shipped directly from the warehouse, only unusual and unforeseen delays would prevent it from being delivered at our site in plenty of time. Thus, we estimate that $P(A \mid W) = 0.95$, where A stands for the event that the shipment arrives on time. On the other hand, back-ordered shipments are highly likely to arrive late, and experience indicates that there is only a 20 percent chance that they will arrive on time; thus $P(A \mid B) = 0.20$.

Now, one of two things must happen for the shipment to arrive on time. Either the order is sent from the warehouse and it arrives on time, or it is back-ordered and it arrives on time. The probability that the order is sent from the warehouse *and* arrives on time is given by Rule 5 to be

$$P(W \text{ and } A) = P(W)P(A \mid W) = (0.75)(0.95) = 0.7125$$

The probability that the order is back-ordered *and* arrives on time is similarly given by Rule 5 to be

$$P(B \text{ and } A) = P(B)P(A \mid B) = (0.25)(0.20) = 0.0500$$

Finally, the probability that the order arrives on time is the probability that it is either shipped from the warehouse and arrives on time *or* it is back-ordered and arrives on time. In other words,

$$P(A) = P(W \text{ and } A, \text{ or } B \text{ and } A)$$

Applying the special law of addition (Axiom 3), we obtain

$$P(A) = P(W \text{ and } A) + P(B \text{ and } A)$$

Note that we can apply the special law of addition in this instance because the order could not both have come from the warehouse and have been back-ordered (unless we had an unusually inefficient supplier). We have already calculated the required probabilities; substituting we obtain

$$
\begin{aligned}
P(A) &= P(W)P(A \mid W) + P(B)P(A \mid B) \\
&= (0.75)(0.95) + (0.25)(0.20) \\
&= 0.7125 + 0.0500 \\
&= 0.7625
\end{aligned}
$$

This seemingly complicated result could easily have been constructed from the diagram in Figure 9. The probability of the final outcome *A* is obtained by multiplying the two probabilities on each branch of the tree shown in the figure, and adding the results over all branches. More generally, this method of solving problems in which the ultimate outcome depends on outcomes at various intermediate stages is called the *Rule of Elimination*. We can visualize this rule by constructing a "tree" like the one shown in Figure 9, in

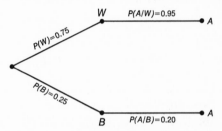

FIGURE 9 / *"Tree" for Warehouse Problem*

which the probability of the final outcome *A* is given by the sum of the products of the probabilities corresponding to each individual branch.

To interpret this result, observe that the probability that the order would arrive on time is 0.95 if we *know* that it was shipped from the warehouse, and this probability is only 0.20 if we *know* that it was back-ordered. Unfortunately, when we placed the order, we had no way of knowing which of these two intermediate events would occur. Thus, our best estimate of the probability of the order's arrival on time is 0.7625, the result we obtained by applying the Rule of Elimination.

Now let us consider a related, and perhaps more interesting problem. The order has arrived on time. What is the probability that it was back-ordered? In symbols, we are interested in evaluating $P(B \mid A)$, the probability of B *given* A. Applying Rule 5, we can write

$$P(B \mid A) = \frac{P(A \text{ and } B)}{P(A)} = \frac{P(B)P(A \mid B)}{P(A)}$$

But, by the Rule of Elimination, we have

$$P(A) = P(W)P(A \mid W) + P(B)P(A \mid B)$$

Substituting this quantity for $P(A)$ in the formula for $P(B \mid A)$, we obtain

$$P(B \mid A) = \frac{P(B)P(A \mid B)}{P(W)P(A \mid W) + P(B)P(A \mid B)}$$

We have already calculated separate values for both the numerator and the denominator of this expression; we have obtained $P(B)P(A \mid B) = 0.0500$ and $P(A) = 0.7625$. Thus,

$$P(B \mid A) = \frac{0.0500}{0.7625} = 0.0656$$

This result has a very interesting interpretation. Note that the unconditional probability of B, the probability that the order had to be back-ordered, was originally given as 0.25. However, *once it is established that the order has arrived on time,* the probability that it was back-ordered is reduced to 0.0656. In other words, the addition of collateral information about the final disposition of this order has reduced the probability of back-ordering by a factor of nearly 4.

The probability of back-ordering, $P(B)$, is a *prior probability.* It represents our estimate of the probability of an event prior to any further observations. The conditional probability P*(B | A)* is an *a posteriori prob-ability,* which represents the probability of *B* after col-lateral information is obtained about whether the order has arrived on time.

In making business decisions, we often are concerned about how our prior estimates of probabilities are modi-fied by collateral information. The rule that we have derived for finding the *a posteriori* probability of *B* is a special instance of *Bayes' rule.* More generally, Bayes' rule is a formula for finding the *a posteriori* probabil-ity of an event, when the prior probability of that event is known.

As a further illustration of Bayes' rule, let us consider the following example. At the beginning of the day our inventory of a certain perishable item could have con-sisted of 0, 1, 2, 3, 4, or 5 units, with probabilities of 0.1, 0.1, 0.2, 0.3, 0.2, and 0.1, respectively. The prob-abilities that the stock will be sold out at the end of the day depend upon the initial inventory. If there are no items initially in inventory, this probability will equal 1. If there is 1 item, we shall assume that there is a 0.9 chance that it will be sold. For 2 items the chance is 0.8, for 3 it is 0.7, for 4 it is 0.6, and for 5 it is 0.5. At the end of the day we observe that the stock has been sold out, but we did not know the size of the stock at the beginning of the day. What is the probability that it consisted of 3 items?

To solve this problem, we make use of the tree shown in Figure 10. To apply Bayes' rule, first we mul-tiply the probabilities on the branch corresponding to 3 items stocked, to obtain $(0.3)(0.7) = 0.21$. Then we divided this number by the result of multiplying the 2 probabilities on each of the 6 branches and adding. We get

$$P(3 \text{ units stocked} \mid \text{sold out}) =$$

$$\frac{(.3)(.7)}{(.1)(1.0) + (.1)(.9) + (.2)(.8) + (.3)(.7) + (.2)(.6) + (.1)(.5)}$$

$$= \frac{.21}{.73} = 0.288$$

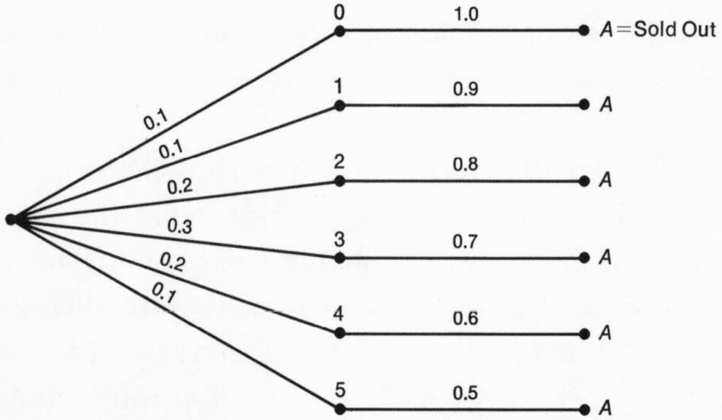

FIGURE 10 / "Tree" for Inventory Problem

This result is interpreted as follows. The prior probability that 3 units were stocked is 0.3. If it is *known* that the stock is sold out, however, application of Bayes' rule shows that this probability is reduced slightly to 0.288. In other words, the *a posteriori* probability of the same event equals 0.288. Apparently the additional information that the stock is sold out was not too helpful in this case—it did not materially change the chance that 3 units were stocked.

CHAPTER 6

Alligator Pears and Distributed Ignorance

The word "random" is one of the most used—and least understood—words in statistics. The phrase "chosen at random" usually evokes in our minds some notion of equal probabilities, and it is loosely tied to the idea of fairness. Actually, the world "random" is a highly technical term that is used in several different contexts in statistics. In this chapter we shall use it in connection with another word that comes to us from mathematics, the word "variable," and discuss *random variables*. In the next chapter we shall discuss *random samples,* and hopefully gain a deeper understanding of the concept of randomness in its more commonly used form.

When we discussed probabilities in Chapter 5, we observed that a probability is a number assigned to an outcome of an experiment, the word "experiment" being used in its broadest possible sense. We also observed that, before we could do anything useful with the concept of probability, it was necessary to find some way to assign a probability value to each of the possible outcomes comprising the sample space of the particular experiment under consideration. As you might have already guessed, this can be a stupendous task. For example, if we take into account the order in which heads and tails appear, more than 1,000 outcomes are possible when a coin is tossed only 10 times. For 50 tosses, the number of outcomes is astronomical.

In most practical problems we are not really interested in the precise nature of each possible outcome. Instead, we are interested in some specific characteristic of these outcomes. For example, if we toss a coin 10 times, we may be interested only in the number of times a head appears, or in the number of times that a tail follows a head, and so forth. As a further illustration, suppose we consider the balance sheets of 100 companies. Even if we concern ourselves only with the annual earnings of each company, the number of possible outcomes (earnings in dollars) is stupendous. Instead, however, our purpose may be merely to determine how many of these companies showed a profit. Thus, the number of events whose probabilities are of real interest to us is only 101, namely, 0, 1, 2, . . . , 100.

There is a host of similar problems, in which we *assign a meaningful number* to each outcome of an experiment (each point in a sample space). The assignment of such numerical values to the points in a sample space results in what is called a *random variable*. This somewhat technical idea of associating a numerical value with each outcome in a sample space results in what mathematicians call a "set function." Thus, we see that a random variable is something like an alligator pear, which is neither an alligator nor a pear (it is an avocado). A random variable is neither random nor variable; it is a set function defined on a sample space.

Probability Distributions

To illustrate how we can define a meaningful numerical-valued random variable on a sample space, let us consider a simple example in which a coin is tossed four times. The following is a list of the 16 possible outcomes of the experiment:

```
H H H H  (4)    T H H H  (3)    H T T H  (2)    T H T T  (1)
H H H T  (3)    H H T T  (2)    T H T H  (2)    T T H T  (1)
H H T H  (3)    H T H T  (2)    T T H H  (2)    T T T H  (1)
H T H H  (3)    T H H T  (2)    H T T T  (1)    T T T T  (0)
```

Let us assume that the coin was manufactured and tossed in such a way that it is reasonable to suppose that each outcome is as likely as any of the others; to put it differently, the probability of any one of these outcomes equals 1/16.

Suppose, now, that we are really only interested in the *number of heads* that come up when we make the four tosses. Next to each of the 16 outcomes we have placed a number indicating the number of heads corresponding to that outcome. In this manner, we have associated a numerical value with each point in the sample space; this association is an example of what we have been calling a random variable. The number itself (0, 1, 2, 3, or 4) is called a *value* of the random variable, and we shall let x stand for some general value picked from this list.

We can now answer the question, "What is the probability that the random variable so defined takes on the value 3?" Since we observe that there are 4 points in the sample space corresponding to the number 3, that each has the probability 1/16, and that these are disjoint events (no two outcomes could have occurred on the same set of four tosses), we can use the Special Law of Addition (page 43) to calculate the probability that any one of those four outcomes could have occurred. We obtain

$P(HHHT \text{ or } HHTH \text{ or } HTHH \text{ or } THHH)$

$$= \frac{1}{16} + \frac{1}{16} + \frac{1}{16} + \frac{1}{16} = \frac{1}{4}$$

We can similarly perform this calculation for each of the remaining values that the random variable can assume. Let us summarize these calculations in a table of the following form:

x	0	1	2	3	4
P(x)	1/16	4/16	6/16	4/16	1/16

In this table we have associated with each value, x, of the random variable the probability that this value will be assumed. Thus, the probability that x will assume the value 0 is 1/16, the probability that x will assume the value 1 is 4/16, and so forth. It is important to note that these associated probabilities add to 1 when summed over all the values that x can take on. This new table, associating probabilities with values of a random variable, defines what is called a *probability distribution function.*

By way of general definition, if we are given a sample space, if we define a random variable on this sample space, and if we find the probability that the random variable will take on each of its possible values, then we have defined a probability distribution function.

All this may appear to be a highly technical abstraction, but it is one of the most important ideas of probability, and it is the bridge over which we may walk from the highly mathematical theory of probability to the basic ideas of statistics. It is the concept of random variables and their associated probability distributions that allows us to make practical applications of probabilities. If it weren't for these concepts, it would be virtually impossible to make general statements about past experience and to build even the simplest of probability models based on experience.

Important special applications of these concepts are developed in Chapter 7. In the remainder of this chapter we shall discuss a small number of special probability distributions, those that have broadest applications to business and economic statistics. Statisticians have defined and studied the properties of many probability distributions, each having its own special properties and its own special applications. Observations of natural phenomena, physical and biological measurements, social, business, and economic data—all have been found to conform closely to the rules suggested by one or more of these probability distributions. It requires educated intuition and wide experience to determine which of all the possible probability laws is the appropriate one to apply in any given situation.

The results of any statistical analysis are no better than the assumptions upon which they are founded. We generally begin by assuming that the data will follow a certain probability law (probability distribution) and work from there. In almost any application, it is highly unlikely that the data will *exactly* follow the probability law assumed. In fact, we think of this probability law only as an idealized abstraction, which is only approximately realized in nature. Remarkably, many useful and empirically verifiable results can be based on such assumptions.

The Binomial Distribution

An important class of decision problems deals with a set of "trials" of an event. For example, we may wish to know the probability of obtaining 6 heads and 5 tails in 11 tosses of a balanced coin, or the probability that 30 out of 50 voters will favor a certain candidate, or the probability that 4 out of 5 transistors will last at least 1,000 hours. In each case we have a given number of "trials," and we are concerned with the probability of obtaining a certain number of "successes."

The solution to this problem depends primarily upon what assumptions we make about the trials. The problem can be stated more satisfactorily if we invent some notation. Accordingly, let us denote the number of trials by n, and the number of successes in the n trials by x. We shall make the following assumptions about these trials:

1. Any given trial can result in one of only two possible outcomes.
2. The probability of a success is the same for each trial.
3. The outcome of any given trial is not influenced by the outcome of the preceding trials.

Examples of sequences of trials that may reasonably well approximate these assumptions are successive tosses of a coin, successive failures of transistors, the selection of balls from a bowl of black and white balls *with replacement,* the sequence of hits and misses when a rifleman shoots at a target, and—believe it or not—the sequence of plus and minus deviations (sometimes called "ticks") in the price of a stock in successive trades.

The preference of a list of voters for, or in opposition to, a certain candidate may or may not satisfy these assumptions. If the names appear on the list in a "random order," the assumptions are satisfied. On the other hand, if the voters happen to appear on the register in alphabetical order, husbands and wives will be listed together and in many cases will influence each other's voting habits. In other words, the series of trials will not be independent.

The process of drawing balls from a bowl of black and white balls *without replacement* violates the assumptions listed above, because the probability that a white ball will be drawn changes from trial to trial.

The set of outcomes resulting when a die is rolled repeatedly does not belong to the class of trials that we are discussing, because more than two outcomes are possible for any given trial. The sequence of profits (or losses) of a given company from year to year probably does not satisfy these assumptions because it would seem more likely for a profitable year to be followed by a profitable year than by an unprofitable one.

The word "random" sometimes is applied to sequences of trials so defined. As we have seen, this is a very special kind of randomness; in essence we are talking about "memoryless" trials that can have only two possible outcomes.

Now let us tackle the problem of finding the probability of x successes in n trials so defined. We shall be able to obtain the solution by applying the laws of probability given in Chapter 5. We shall denote a success by the letter S and a failure by the letter F. First let us consider any *fixed* arrangement of x successes and $n - x$ failures. For simplicity, we shall suppose that the x successes occurred first, followed by $n - x$ failures, as follows:

$$\underbrace{S, S, \ldots, S,}_{x} \underbrace{F, F, \ldots, F}_{n - x}$$

Suppose each success (S) has the probability p of occurring. Then, by Rule 1 on page 62, each failure has the probability $1 - p$ of occurring. The probability of obtaining a success on the first trial *and* a success on the second trial, *and* a success on the third trial, . . . , *and* a success on the trial numbered x can be found by using the special law of multiplication, because the outcome of each trial is independent of the outcomes of the preceding trials. This probability is simply the product of x probabilities, each equal to p. Similarly, the probability of obtaining $n - x$ failures is the product of $n - x$ factors $(1 - p)$. Thus, we can write the probability of this sequence in the form

$$\underbrace{pp \ldots p}_{x} \times \underbrace{(1 - p)(1 - p) \ldots (1 - p)}_{n - x} = p^x(1 - p)^{n-x}$$

This last result gives the probability of obtaining x successes and $n - x$ failures *in a given order*. But we are not concerned with the *order* of the Ss and the Fs; we are interested only in the number of Ss contained in the sequence. Clearly, no matter what the order, any sequence containing x Ss (and $n - x$ Fs) will have the same probability, namely $p^x(1 - p)^{n-x}$. Since no two distinct sequences could have occurred in the same set of trials, the probability that one *or* another of these sequences occurs can be obtained by adding this quantity a number of times equal to the number of such sequences. (This follows from the special law of addition for probabilities given on page 61). To count them, we can ask the number of ways that we can distribute the x Ss in a sequence of n trials. Without going into detail, let us simply state that the number of ways that we can distribute x successes in n trials is equal to

$$\binom{n}{x} = \frac{n(n - 1) \ldots (n - x + 1)}{x(x - 1) \ldots 3 \times 2 \times 1}$$

This number, sometimes called the *binomial coeffi-*

cient, is tabulated in Table 10 for values of n up to 10. Note that each number in this table can be obtained by

TABLE *10* / *Pascal's Triangle—Values of the Binomial Coefficient* $\binom{n}{x}$

n	0	1	2	3	4	5	6	7	8	9	10
0	1										
1	1	1									
2	1	2	1								
3	1	3	3	1							
4	1	4	6	4	1						
5	1	5	10	10	5	1					
6	1	6	15	20	15	6	1				
7	1	7	21	35	35	21	7	1			
8	1	8	28	56	70	56	28	8	1		
9	1	9	36	84	126	126	84	36	9	1	
10	1	10	45	120	210	252	210	120	45	10	1

adding the number appearing directly above it to the number appearing above it and to the immediate left. For example,

$$126 = 70 + 56$$

or

$$\binom{9}{4} = \binom{8}{4} + \binom{8}{3}$$

This interesting fact was discovered and proved by a mathematician named Blaise Pascal and the resulting table is called "Pascal's triangle."

Returning to our problem, recall that, if we can find the number of ways that we could distribute x Ss among n trials, we can multiply this number by

$p^x(1-p)^{n-x}$ to obtain the probability of x successes in n trials. Accordingly, the probability of obtaining x successes (in any order) in n trials of the type described is given by

$$P(x) = \binom{n}{x} p^x(1-p)^{n-x}$$

In this formula, x is the number of successes, n is the number of trials, p is the fixed probability of a success on any given trial.

The formula given for $P(x)$ is called the *binomial distribution*. Actually this formula defines a *family* of binomial distributions; histograms depicting two members of this family are shown in Figure 11. This family of distributions forms the basis for much of the work done in industrial acceptance sampling. Mil-Std 105D, the widely used government standard for procurement of materials, gives a collection of acceptance and rejection tables for use in sampling of lots of manufactured products; these tables are based on the binomial distribution.

To give immediate application to our discovery, let us return to the problem considered earlier, in which we tossed an "honest" coin four times and asked for the probability of obtaining exactly three heads. By direct enumeration we have already found that the answer to this problem is 1/4. Let's tackle it again with the use of our formula. In this case p, the probability of a head on any given toss, is assumed to equal 1/2 (the assumption of equal likelihood again). Because we are tossing the coin four times, $n = 4$; and because we are inter-

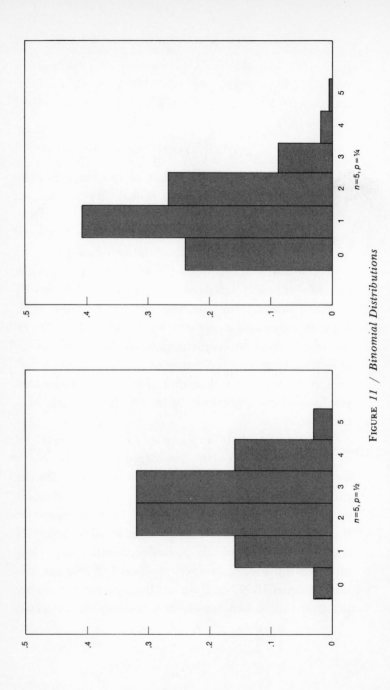

FIGURE 11 / *Binomial Distributions*

ested in the probability of exactly three heads, $x = 3$. First, entering Table 10 with $n = 4$ and $x = 3$, we observe that

$$\binom{4}{3} = 4$$

Thus we obtain

$$P(3) = \binom{4}{3}\left(\frac{1}{2}\right)^{3}\left(1 - \frac{1}{2}\right)^{1}$$

$$= 4 \times \frac{1}{8} \times \frac{1}{2} = \frac{1}{4}$$

which, to our vast relief, is exactly the answer we obtained earlier.

Why should we have bothered to go through all this nonsense with formulas and tables when we could have derived the answer by direct enumeration as we did earlier? The answer becomes fairly evident when we are given the problem of finding the probability of exactly 7 heads when 10 coins are tossed. To obtain this answer by direct enumeration we would have to list all the possible events in the resulting sample space, a total of 1,024. Then, corresponding to each event, we would have to write down the number of heads, thus defining the required random variable. Then, we would have to find the probability of each of these 1,024 events. (On the assumption of equal likelihood it equals $1/1024$.) Finally, we would have to add these probabilities over all of the outcomes corresponding to each value of the random variable.

It is a lot less work to do it as follows. Substituting $n = 10$, $x = 7$, and $p = 1/2$ in our formula, we get

$$P(7) = \binom{10}{7} \left(\frac{1}{2}\right)^7 \left(1 - \frac{1}{2}\right)^3$$

$$= 120 \times \frac{1}{128} \times \frac{1}{8}$$

$$= 0.1172$$

Through mathematical manipulations with the formula defining the binomial distribution, it is possible to show that the mean value of a binomially distributed random variable equals np and that its standard deviation equals $\sqrt{np(1-p)}$. Thus, for example, if the probability of success on a given trial equals 1/3, and we perform 75 trials of an event, we would expect an average of $1/3 \times 75 = 25$ successes. The standard deviation of the number of successes in these 75 trials would therefore be

$$\sqrt{75 \times \frac{1}{3} \times \frac{2}{3}} = 4.1$$

Referring to Table 8 we observe that it would be highly unlikely to obtain a number of successes differing from the mean value (25) by more than three standard deviations (12.3). In other words, we should be highly surprised if these 75 trials resulted in less than 13 or more than 37 successes.

Suppose a vendor delivered to your factory a lot of 1,000 manufactured items with the claim that the lot contained no more than 2 percent defectives. Before accepting and paying for this lot, your purchasing agent wishes to check this claim. Accordingly, he selects a sample of 100 items from the lot, making sure that the sample is representative. (For instance, he might select each 10th item by serial number.) If the proportion of defectives is indeed 2 percent, he would expect to observe $.02 \times 100 = 2$ defective items in the sample. The standard deviation of the number of items of defectives in the sample is $\sqrt{100 \times .02 \times .98} = 1.4$. On selecting this sample of 100 items and examining each carefully, he finds that the sample contains 8 defectives. Is this evidence upon which to reject the lot, claiming that the true proportion of defectives in the submitted lot could not have been at most 2 percent?

As the expected number of defectives is 2, and the standard deviation is 1.4, it would have been extremely unlikely to obtain a sample containing more than $2 +$ (3×1.4), or approximately 6, defectives. Because your purchasing agent found 8 defectives, there are only two possibilities. Either he was the victim of extraordinarily bad luck, that is, the lot actually contained only 2 percent defectives and the sample contained as many as 8 defectives by virtue of chance alone, or else there were in fact more than 2 percent defectives in the lot.

At this point, the science of statistics steps out and managerial policy-making steps in. Are you willing to accept that a "near miracle" occurred? Or is it your decision to send the lot back to the vendor? (Of course, alternate decisions are available to you. For example, you may be in serious need of this shipment and are willing to accept the added cost of culling out the defective items in return for a price concession.)

In this little example, we have the germ of a typical statistical decision-making problem. By application of the binomial distribution, we have been able to say something about the chance that the vendor's claim is correct. Based on the odds thus calculated, we are in a better position to make a rational decision.

The Poisson Distribution

Suppose you are in the business of providing services to the public on a first-come, first-serve basis. You may be a banker and are concerned with providing enough tellers to assist your customers in transacting without undue delay their deposits, withdrawals, and other bank business. You might be running a gasoline station and are concerned about the rate at which automobiles arrive for service. You might be in the process of deciding how many check-out stations to include in the design of a supermarket. You might be concerned about the number of trunk telephone lines to provide for your business office. All of these examples have in common the problem of providing service that is responsive to the arrival rate of customers who do not arrive in any particular pattern. Loosely speaking, we could say that the customers arrive "at random."

What we really mean is this. We can assume that there is a very, very large number of potential customers in the world and that at any moment there is a small but fixed probability that one of them will require service. For example, the set of all potential customers might consist of all depositors at a given bank. At any one moment the probability is extremely low that any specific customer will require service, but the number of customers is so large that it is likely that at least one of them will require service in a given short interval of time. This begins to look something like a sequence of trials of the kind described in the preceding section, in which n, the number of trials, is extremely large (and probably unknown) and the probability of a "success" (the arrival of a customer requiring service) for any *given* customer is extremely small (and probably unknown).

We shall further assume that there is no "run on the bank," or other similar situation that causes the presence or absence of one customer to make the presence or absence of any other customer more or less likely. In other words, we seem to have satisfied all of the assumptions for the kind of trials underlying the binomial distribution; namely, there are only two possible outcomes of any given trial (the given customer arrives or does not arrive), the probability of success is constant from trial to trial (no one customer is any more or less likely to arrive than any other), and the outcome of any trial does not depend on the outcomes of the preceding trials.

If we knew the values of n and p, we could compute the probability of any given number of customers arriving for service in a fixed period of time (number of trials). Unfortunately, all we know about them is that n is very large and p is very small. Nonetheless, it is possible to tackle this problem. Mathematicians have shown that—as n becomes indefinitely large, p becomes arbitrarily small, and the mean np remains fixed at the value λ (lambda)—the formula for the binomial distribution becomes

$$f(x) = \frac{e^{-\lambda}\lambda^x}{x(x-1)\ldots 3 \times 2 \times 1}$$

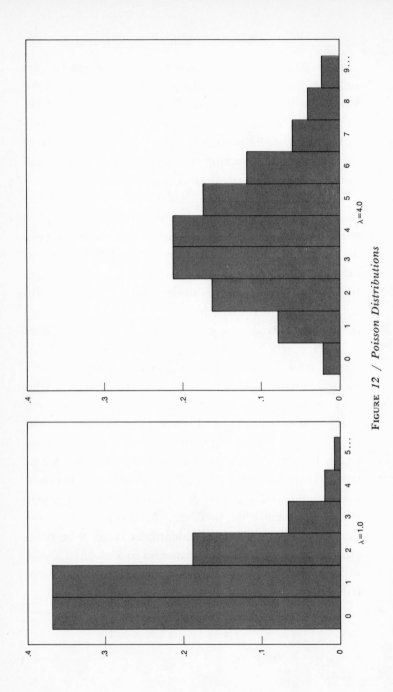

FIGURE 12 / *Poisson Distributions*

In this formula, λ is interpretable as the mean number of arrivals in a fixed period of time, and e is a constant (the base of the system of natural logarithms) whose value is approximated by 2.718. The resulting distribution, named after its discoverer, is called the Poisson distribution. Two members of the family of Poisson distributions are depicted in Figure 12.

A table of values of the Poisson distribution is given in Table 11. This table gives *sums* of values of the Poisson distribution function up to x terms for several in-

TABLE *11* / *Poisson Distribution Function*

x \ λ	1	2	3	4	5	6	7	8	9	10
0	.368	.135	.050	.018	.007	.002	.001	.000	.000	.000
1	.736	.406	.199	.092	.040	.017	.007	.003	.001	.000
2	.920	.677	.423	.238	.125	.062	.030	.014	.006	.003
3	.981	.857	.647	.433	.265	.151	.082	.042	.021	.010
4	.996	.947	.815	.629	.440	.285	.173	.100	.055	.029
5	.999	.983	.916	.785	.616	.446	.301	.191	.116	.067
6	1.000	.995	.966	.889	.762	.606	.450	.313	.207	.130
7		.999	.988	.949	.867	.744	.599	.453	.324	.220
8		1.000	.996	.979	.932	.847	.729	.593	.456	.333
9			.999	.992	.968	.916	.830	.717	.587	.458
10			1.000	.997	.986	.957	.901	.816	.706	.583
11				.999	.995	.980	.947	.888	.803	.697
12				1.000	.998	.991	.973	.936	.876	.792
13					.999	.996	.987	.966	.926	.864
14					1.000	.999	.994	.983	.959	.917
15						.999	.998	.992	.978	.951
16						1.000	.999	.996	.989	.973
17							1.000	.998	.995	.986
18								.999	.998	.993
19								1.000	.999	.997
20									1.000	.998
21										.999
22										1.000

teger values of λ. As an example of its use, consider the following situation. The number of customers arriving at a small-town bank is such that in any given hour it follows the Poisson distribution, with a mean arrival rate of 10 customers per hour. What is the probability that, in any given one-hour period, more than 15 customers will have arrived?

To answer this question let us consult Table 11, entering it with the value $\lambda = 10$, the mean arrival rate. Although we are interested in the probability that *more than 15 customers* will arrive in a given hour, to make use of the table we must first find the probability that *up to 15 customers* will arrive. Table 11 gives this probability at 0.951, and, applying Rule 1 for probabilities (page 62), we calculate that the probability of more than 15 customers arriving equals $1 - 0.951$, or 0.049. In other words, if the bank is able to serve up to 15 customers arriving in any given hour, its facilities would be placed under unusual stress only about 5 percent of the time.

The Poisson distribution has the mean value λ, as we already have seen. In addition, its standard deviation equals $\sqrt{\lambda}$. Thus, for example, if the mean arrival rate of customers at the bank were 4 per hour instead of 10, Chebychev assures us that the odds strongly favor the arrival of no more than 10 customers ($\lambda + 3\sqrt{\lambda}$, or $4 + 3\sqrt{4}$) in a given hour. In fact, the exact probability is given by Table 11 to be 0.997.

The Poisson distribution also has been successfully applied to problems dealing with imperfections in a continuous electrolytic process, to breakdowns in a computer, to gamma radiation emitted by a radioactive substance, and to the incidence of hurricanes on the East Coast of the United States. Perhaps one of its most interesting and widespread applications arises in connection with queuing problems, such as the problem that we briefly discussed, of customers arriving at a bank. This distribution is another example of a probability distribution, derived from purely theoretical arguments, that can be applied successfully to an amazingly wide variety of practical problems.

The Normal Distribution

The normal distribution is another distribution function that, in theory, arises from the binomial distribution. As in the case of the Poisson distribution, we shall think of n, the number of trials, as being indefinitely large. However, we shall now abandon the idea that p, the probability of a "success" on any given trial, is small. When we do this, the number of bars in the histogram of the corresponding binomial distribution (see Figure 11) becomes indefinitely large, and if we think of the bases of these bars as becoming smaller and smaller, the outlines of the resulting histograms become closer and closer to the symmetrical, bell-shaped curve shown in Figure 13.

When we discussed the mean of an empirical distribution in Chapter 3, we observed that it was located at the center of gravity of the distribution. The same fact holds true for a theoretical distribution, and it follows that the mean of the normal distribution is located di-

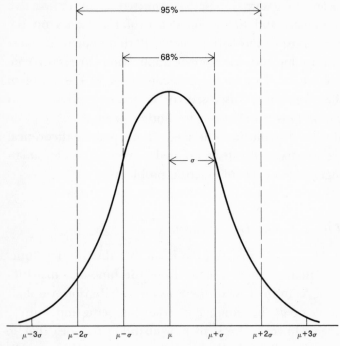

FIGURE *13* / *A Normal Distribution*

rectly beneath the highest point of the symmetric bell curve. To distinguish this theoretical mean from the mean of a sample (an empirical mean) we shall use the symbol μ (mu) instead of $\bar{x}$, as shown in Figure 13.

The standard deviation of this distribution also can be located by the geometry of the curve. The two points at which the bell-shaped curve ceases to be convex and begins to be concave are called "points of inflection." The distance along the base line (horizontal axis) between the mean, μ, and the point directly beneath either point of inflection equals one standard deviation.

As we used μ instead of $\bar{x}$ to denote the mean of a theoretical distribution, we shall use the symbol σ (sigma) instead of S to denote the standard deviation of a theoretical distribution.

The relationship between σ, the standard deviation, and the values that can be assumed by an observation is relatively easy to observe in the case of the normal distribution. If the data are normally distributed and σ is large, the distribution is "spread out" and the likelihood that an observation assumes a value far away from the mean increases. On the other hand, if σ is small, the distribution is "taller and skinnier," and it would be quite unlikely for an observation to assume values far from the mean.

According to Axiom 2 for probabilities (page 60), the probability of the sample space must equal 1. When we apply this axiom to a probability distribution like the normal distribution, it implies that the *area* under the curve representing the probability distribution must equal 1. In fact, *the area under the curve between any two points on the base line represents the probability that the random variable will assume values between those points.*

As in the case of the binomial and Poisson distributions, there is an entire family of normal distributions. Each normal distribution is symmetric and bell-shaped, and each encloses an area of 1. If μ, the mean, is increased, the entire curve is shifted to the right; if μ is decreased, the entire curve is shifted to the left. In addition, if σ is increased or decreased, the "spread" of the distribution is correspondingly changed. Because both μ and σ can assume infinitely many values (at least theoretically), there is an infinite number of different normal distributions.

In order to find the probability that an observation coming from a normal distribution takes on a value between two given limits, it is necessary to find the area under the appropriate normal curve (the normal curve corresponding to the given μ and σ) between these two limits. This very complicated task has been made easier by tables of normal-curve areas. As there is an infinite number of possible normal distributions, one would expect that an infinite number of tables of areas would be required. To avoid the necessity of constructing so many tables (and the consequent strain on the national economy), a simple trick can be used.

Suppose we let x stand for the value of a random variable having the normal distribution with mean μ and standard deviation σ. Suppose we now "code" this value, much as we coded empirical data when we computed $\bar{x}$ and S in Chapters 3 and 4. This time we shall subtract the mean μ and divide the result of the standard deviation σ, obtaining

$$z = \frac{x - \mu}{\sigma}$$

It can be proved mathematically that the resulting quantity has the normal distribution with the mean 0 and the standard deviation 1, called the *standard normal curve*. This process of subtracting the mean and dividing by the standard deviation is called *standardiza-*

tion, and the resulting quantity, z, is called a *standard normal variable.*

Areas under the standard normal curve are tabulated in Table 12. For values of the standard normal variable z from 0.00 to 3.49 this table gives the area under the standard normal curve to the left of z. Turning to this table, we observe for example that when z equals 0.00 the area given by the corresponding entry in the table is 0.5000. This result is no surprise, because we know that the standard normal curve has a mean of 0, and, because of symmetry, half the area should be to the left of 0.

If we look at the table entry corresponding to $z = 1.00$ (one standard deviation to the right of the mean), we observe the value 0.8413. In other words, the area to the left of $\mu + \sigma$ equals 0.8413. As the area to the left of the mean equals .5000, it follows that the area *between* μ and $\mu + \sigma$ equals $0.8413 - 0.5000 = 0.3413$; and, by symmetry, the area between $\mu - \sigma$ and μ also equals 0.3413. Thus, the area under any normal curve between $\mu - \sigma$ and $\mu + \sigma$ equals 2×0.3413, or 0.6826. In other words, approximately 68.3 percent of the time a normally distributed random variable will assume a value within one standard deviation of its mean (see Figure 13).

Similarly, for $z = 2$, we observe that the area given in the table is 0.9772. Thus, the area between μ and $\mu + 2\sigma$ is 0.4772, and we similarly conclude from the symmetry of the normal curve that approximately 95.4 percent of the values of a random variable having a

TABLE 12 / Normal Distribution Function

z	0.00	0.01	0.02	0.03	0.04	0.05	0.06	0.07	0.08	0.09
0.0	0.5000	0.5040	0.5080	0.5120	0.5160	0.5199	0.5239	0.5279	0.5319	0.5359
0.1	0.5398	0.5438	0.5478	0.5517	0.5557	0.5596	0.5636	0.5675	0.5714	0.5753
0.2	0.5793	0.5832	0.5871	0.5910	0.5948	0.5987	0.6026	0.6064	0.6103	0.6141
0.3	0.6179	0.6217	0.6255	0.6293	0.6331	0.6368	0.6406	0.6443	0.6480	0.6517
0.4	0.6554	0.6591	0.6628	0.6664	0.6700	0.6736	0.6772	0.6808	0.6844	0.6879
0.5	0.6915	0.6950	0.6985	0.7019	0.7054	0.7088	0.7123	0.7157	0.7190	0.7224
0.6	0.7257	0.7291	0.7324	0.7357	0.7389	0.7422	0.7454	0.7486	0.7517	0.7549
0.7	0.7580	0.7611	0.7642	0.7673	0.7704	0.7734	0.7764	0.7794	0.7823	0.7852
0.8	0.7881	0.7910	0.7939	0.7967	0.7995	0.8023	0.8051	0.8078	0.8106	0.8133
0.9	0.8159	0.8186	0.8212	0.8238	0.8264	0.8289	0.8315	0.8340	0.8365	0.8389
1.0	0.8413	0.8438	0.8461	0.8485	0.8508	0.8531	0.8554	0.8577	0.8599	0.8621
1.1	0.8643	0.8665	0.8686	0.8708	0.8729	0.8749	0.8770	0.8790	0.8810	0.8830
1.2	0.8849	0.8869	0.8888	0.8907	0.8925	0.8944	0.8962	0.8980	0.8997	0.9015
1.3	0.9032	0.9049	0.9066	0.9082	0.9099	0.9115	0.9131	0.9147	0.9162	0.9177
1.4	0.9192	0.9207	0.9222	0.9236	0.9251	0.9265	0.9279	0.9292	0.9306	0.9319
1.5	0.9332	0.9345	0.9357	0.9370	0.9382	0.9394	0.9406	0.9418	0.9429	0.9441
1.6	0.9452	0.9463	0.9474	0.9484	0.9495	0.9505	0.9515	0.9525	0.9535	0.9545

1.7	0.9554	0.9564	0.9573	0.9582	0.9591	0.9599	0.9608	0.9616	0.9625	0.9633
1.8	0.9641	0.9649	0.9656	0.9664	0.9671	0.9678	0.9686	0.9693	0.9699	0.9706
1.9	0.9713	0.9719	0.9726	0.9732	0.9738	0.9744	0.9750	0.9756	0.9761	0.9767
2.0	0.9772	0.9778	0.9783	0.9788	0.9793	0.9798	0.9803	0.9808	0.9812	0.9817
2.1	0.9821	0.9826	0.9830	0.9834	0.9838	0.9842	0.9846	0.9850	0.9854	0.9857
2.2	0.9861	0.9864	0.9868	0.9871	0.9875	0.9878	0.9881	0.9884	0.9887	0.9890
2.3	0.9893	0.9896	0.9898	0.9901	0.9904	0.9906	0.9909	0.9911	0.9913	0.9916
2.4	0.9918	0.9920	0.9922	0.9925	0.9927	0.9929	0.9931	0.9932	0.9934	0.9936
2.5	0.9938	0.9940	0.9941	0.9943	0.9945	0.9946	0.9948	0.9949	0.9951	0.9952
2.6	0.9953	0.9955	0.9956	0.9957	0.9959	0.9960	0.9961	0.9962	0.9963	0.9964
2.7	0.9965	0.9966	0.9967	0.9968	0.9969	0.9970	0.9971	0.9972	0.9973	0.9974
2.8	0.9974	0.9975	0.9976	0.9977	0.9977	0.9978	0.9979	0.9979	0.9980	0.9981
2.9	0.9981	0.9982	0.9982	0.9983	0.9984	0.9984	0.9985	0.9985	0.9986	0.9986
3.0	0.9987	0.9987	0.9987	0.9988	0.9988	0.9989	0.9989	0.9989	0.9990	0.9990
3.1	0.9990	0.9991	0.9991	0.9991	0.9992	0.9992	0.9992	0.9992	0.9993	0.9993
3.2	0.9993	0.9993	0.9994	0.9994	0.9994	0.9994	0.9994	0.9995	0.9995	0.9995
3.3	0.9995	0.9995	0.9996	0.9996	0.9996	0.9996	0.9996	0.9996	0.9996	0.9997
3.4	0.9997	0.9997	0.9997	0.9997	0.9997	0.9997	0.9997	0.9997	0.9997	0.9998

normal distribution will lie within two standard deviations of its mean (Figure 13). A similar argument will show that 99.7 percent of the values of a normally distributed random variable will lie within three standard deviations of its mean.

A comparison of these results with Table 8 is very revealing. According to this table, the probability that a random variable having *any* distribution will assume a value more than three standard deviations away from its mean is at most 1/9. If we know that the random variable is normally distributed, however, this probability turns out to be much smaller, namely 1 — 0.997, or 0.003.

As a further illustration of how we may use the table of areas under the standard normal curve to obtain probabilities, let us consider the following example. Suppose we are faced with the decision of whether or not to begin mining operations to recover a certain metal from an ore bed. We have calculated that the operation will not be profitable unless the ore contains at least 3 percent of the metal. In addition, past experience allows us to assume that the percentage of this metal in the ore is approximately normally distributed throughout the region of the deposits.

Before making our decision, we arrange to take several core samples and assay the contents of the ore in each. (We distribute these core samples as evenly as we can over the depth and breadth of the region to be mined.) From these samples we calculate that the mean percentage of metal in the ore is 6 percent and the standard deviation is 2 percent. We are interested in calculating the probability that any portion of this ore bed will yield less than 3 percent. In other words, if x is the true percentage of metal in the ore, we want to know the probability that x will assume a value less than 3 percent.

We can solve this problem with the use of Table 12 by first standardizing the value of x, that is, by converting the distribution of x to a standard normal distribution. Since our estimate of μ is 6 percent, and our estimate of σ is 2 percent, we have

$$z = \frac{3 - 6}{2} = -1.5$$

Unfortunately we do not find $z = -1.5$ in Table 12; however, we can take advantage of the symmetry of the normal curve. From the diagram in Figure 14 and the symmetry of the normal curve, we observe that the area to the right of $z = +1.5$ equals the area to the left of $z = -1.5$. Thus, we shall enter Table 12 with $z = 1.5$, obtaining the entry 0.9332. Remembering that this table gives areas to the *left* of z, we find that the area to the *right* of $z = 1.5$ equals $1 - 0.9332$, or 0.0668. Thus, the area to the left of $z = -1.5$ also equals 0.0668, and we conclude that the probability that any portion of this ore bed will contain less than 3 percent of the metal is 0.0668.

We can give this result another interpretation: that, of all the batches of ore removed from this mine, only about 6.7 percent will contain less than 3 percent of the metal. Incidentally, it follows from symmetry that only 6.7 percent of all the ore removed from this mine will contain more than 10 percent of the metal.

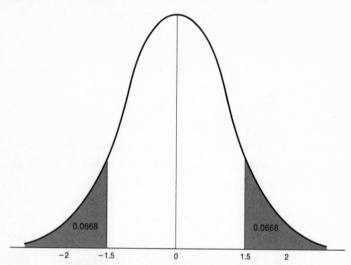

0.0668   0.0668

−2   −1.5   0   1.5   2

FIGURE *14* / *Finding Areas Under the Standard Normal Curve*

The normal distribution plays a central role in statistical decision-making. As we shall see in the next chapter, the empirical means of sufficiently large samples are distributed in repeated samples as if they came from a normal distribution, regardless of the shape of the distribution from which the individual observations were obtained. This amazing and somewhat unexpected result enables us to make inferences about μ, the mean of some *unknown* theoretical distribution, based on $\bar{x}$, the mean of a sufficiently large sample selected from that distribution. By using the table of the standard normal distribution, we shall be able to state the chance that the mean of a new sample would have been different from the mean of the sample at hand by more than a given amount. In other words, we will be in a position to state the reliability of the sample mean at hand.

CHAPTER 7

Decisions, Decisions, Decisions

Statistical inference—arriving at decisions in the face of uncertainty—deals with the problem of making statements about a population based on the results of a random sample. The term *population* comes to us from the science of demography, in which statisticians are concerned with estimating some attribute of a human population.

When we speak of a population, we really are concerned with an appropriately defined random variable. For example, with respect to wage earners in the United States, the random variable may be the annual income of each wage earner.

The population need not represent a collection of humans. It may refer to a collection of households in connection with which we are interested in knowing the number of television sets per household. It may refer to all automobiles on the road at a given time, and the attribute of the population with which we are concerned may be the number of defective safety items. It may refer to all light bulbs that could conceivably be produced by a certain process and we may be interested in the length of life of these bulbs.

The same collection of individuals (whether human or not) can, in fact, give rise to several different random variables and, therefore, to several populations. With respect to households, for example, we get one population when we count the number of television sets, and we get another population when we count the number of children under 12.

Random Samples

In studies in which the population is large, it is very expensive and time-consuming (or it may even be impossible) to observe the value of the required attribute for each and every member. Thus it is desirable to select a "sample" from the population, that is, to choose a small segment that is "representative" of the entire population. The selection of a random sample to represent a population is difficult and must be approached with great care. In choosing a sample, we must not only avoid obvious biases, but also take great pains to make sure that the *entire* population is represented and not just some convenient segment of it. For example, if we were doing a survey to estimate the income of wage earners in a given city, we would clearly get a biased result if we restricted our sample to home owners. Selection from a telephone directory of names of persons to be surveyed might also lead to biased results.

A somewhat dramatic illustration of the dangers of poor sampling practice is provided by the experience of a long defunct magazine, the *Literary Digest*. In 1936 this magazine ran a poll to predict the outcome of the Roosevelt-Landon election. Based on a very large sample selected "at random" from all over the United States, the editors of the *Literary Digest* predicted that Alfred M. Landon would defeat Franklin D. Roosevelt. In the election, however, Roosevelt won a sweeping victory over Landon. At least partially as a result of this highly erroneous prediction, the readers of the *Literary Digest* lost faith in the magazine's credibility, subscriptions dropped drastically, and the magazine soon terminated publication.

What could have caused such a disaster? Wasn't the sample size very large for surveys of this type, and weren't great pains taken to assure "random selection"? Didn't the results of the poll indicate that the election was not even going to be close? (The *Literary Digest* predicted an overwhelming victory for Landon!)

The pollsters fell into the trap of using a very handy but highly unrepresentative list to represent the population. Names were selected from *telephone directories of major cities* throughout the country. In this way the rural vote was largely neglected, and persons who could not afford a telephone in 1936 were entirely omitted from the sample. All the *Literary Digest* proved was that, among those city dwellers who had telephones, Landon was the choice.

A rigorous definition of what statisticians mean by a *random sample* would be somewhat technical. If the population is finite in size, the sample should be chosen so that each member of the population has the same chance of being included in the sample as each other member. Thus, the use of any list or other device for selection of the sample that automatically excludes a certain portion of the population under study could never give rise to a random sample.

There are several ways of assuring the selection of a sample that is at least approximately random. We could serially number the elements of the population from which we are sampling and then select the sample with the aid of a "table of random numbers." If the population size is very large, the use of random numbers can become very laborious and at times virtually impossible. Under certain circumstances, "systematic sampling," such as the selection of every hundredth member of the population, provides a reasonable approximation to a random sample. In general, we should strive to make *proper* use of artificial or mechanical devices for selecting random samples. This method is always preferable to human judgment, as it is extremely difficult to avoid unconscious biases.

The businessman constantly is called upon to make decisions based on the results of opinion polls, market surveys, and other kinds of samples. Before acting on a survey result, he should evaluate the validity of the survey itself. The following are the most important questions to consider in making such an evaluation:

1. Are you sure that both you and the survey organization have exactly the same population in mind?
2. By what methods (lists, maps, etc.) did the survey organization represent this population?
3. Was the sample chosen so that, at least approximately, each member of the population had the same chance of being included?
4. Were you simply given, for example, the size of the audience watching a certain TV show, or the number of potential purchasers favoring your product, or did the results also include a statement about the reliability of these estimates?

The Sample Mean

Suppose we select a random sample of n observations from some population, and we calculate the sample mean, $\bar{x}$. If we had taken a second sample of the same size from the same population, and again calculated $\bar{x}$, could we have expected that the two sample means would have been identical? Both experience and intuition indicate that the sample means will differ, and that these differences may be attributed to chance factors involved in the selection of the samples.

To come to grips with this important idea, let us perform a simple experiment. Take 100 slips of paper, write the number 1 on 10 of them, the number 2 on another 10, and so forth, up to 10 slips bearing the number 10. Put these slips of paper into a bowl and mix them thoroughly. Now, draw a sample of 10 slips of paper from this bowl, replacing each slip of paper after it has been drawn, and reshuffling before selecting the next one. In this way you will have drawn a random sample of size $n = 10$ from a population consisting of the integers from 1 to 10 in equal proportions.

Using the values of the 10 numbers thus drawn, calculate the sample mean, $\bar{x}$; that is, add the numbers drawn and divide by 10. Now, repeat this procedure until you have drawn a total of 50 samples, and have calculated 50 sample means.

When we performed this experiment we obtained the following 50 sample means:

6.0	5.4	6.3	4.2	4.5	7.4	5.4	5.1	4.6	5.4
4.8	6.0	4.1	6.3	5.3	5.8	4.1	4.3	5.9	6.3
5.6	5.0	4.7	4.0	6.8	6.8	4.0	5.6	4.7	4.8
5.8	7.5	5.9	6.5	7.4	5.5	6.3	5.9	4.6	6.3
5.0	5.2	5.7	3.7	3.4	6.6	4.6	3.6	5.4	5.3

Table 13 shows the distribution of these sample means:

TABLE *13* / *Distribution of 50 Sample Means*

$\bar{x}$	Frequency
3.0–3.4	1
3.5–3.9	2
4.0–4.4	6
4.5–4.9	8
5.0–5.4	10
5.5–5.9	9
6.0–6.4	7
6.5–6.9	4
7.0–7.4	2
7.5–7.9	1
	50

This table represents a *sampling distribution*—the distribution of the values of a statistical quantity ($\bar{x}$ in this case) obtained from repeated samples. You may wish to draw a histogram of this distribution. If you do, you will notice that this sampling distribution of $\bar{x}$-values is bell-shaped. To go a step further, let us calculate the mean and the variance of these 50 $\bar{x}$-values, using the methods given for grouped data in Chapters 3 and 4. We obtain

$$\bar{x} = 5.4; \; S^2 = 0.97$$

where the symbol $\bar{x}$ stands for the mean of the sample means.

Suppose we compute like results for the original population from which these 50 mean values were obtained and compare them to the numbers just calculated. This "parent" population consisted of the numbers 1, 2, . . . , 10 in equal proportions. Thus, the mean of the population is $\mu = 5.5$ (the mean of the first 10 positive integers).

We can compute the variance of the parent population as follows. There are 10 slips of paper having the number 1; thus for each of these values the deviation from the mean is $1 - 5.5$, or -4.5. There are 10 slips of paper having the number 2, and therefore having a deviation from the mean equal to $2 - 5.5 = -3.5$, and so forth. Finally, there are 10 slips of paper having the number 10, and corresponding to a deviation from the mean of $10 - 5.5 = 4.5$. The variance is, by definition, the sum of the squared deviations from the mean, divided by 100. (When dealing with a population—that is, when calculating a theoretical variance—we divide by n instead of by $n - 1$.) Therefore, the variance of the parent population is given by

$$\sigma^2 = \frac{10(1 - 5.5)^2 + 10(2 - 5.5)^2 + \ldots + 10(10 - 5.5)^2}{100}$$

$$= 8.25$$

Now let us compare the mean μ and variance σ^2 of the parent population with the mean $\bar{\bar{x}}$ and variance S^2 of the 50 sample means that we calculated by drawing samples of size 10 from this population.

First, we note that μ equals 5.5 and the mean of the 50 sample means equals 5.4. In other words, the sample means seem to cluster about the mean of the original population.

Next, we note that the variance of the original population equals $\sigma^2 = 8.25$, but the variance of the sample means was much smaller, namely 0.97. Thus, it appears that the sample means $\bar{x}$ can be expected to be closer to the population mean μ than an individual observation (they have a smaller variance).

One further comparison also is of interest. The parent population did not have a bell-shaped distribution. In fact, it had a flat distribution—that is, each of its 10 values had the same probability of being drawn, namely, 0.1. Yet the sampling distribution of the means was distinctly bell-shaped, appearing very much like a normal distribution.

In this experiment we obtained an *empirical* sampling distribution, based on only 50 samples of 10 observations each, and the results raise some very important questions. Suppose we were to go on taking additional samples of size 10 until we had taken an enormously large number of such samples (theoretically an infinite number of samples would be required). The distribution thus obtained of values of the sample means is called the *theoretical* sampling distribution of the mean.

For our empirical distribution, based on only 50 samples, we observed that the mean of the sampling distribution ($\bar{\bar{x}} = 5.4$) was nearly equal to the mean of the population from which the samples were obtained ($\mu = 5.5$). We also observed that the variance of our empirical sampling distribution ($S^2 = 0.97$) was smaller than that of the parent population ($\sigma^2 = 8.25$). Finally, we observed that the empirical sampling distribution was similar to a normal distribution.

Would the *theoretical* sampling distribution of the mean, based on an infinite number of samples instead of merely 50, have had the same properties? That is, would its mean be equal (or nearly equal) to μ? Would its variance have been smaller than σ^2? Would it be a normal distribution?

These questions have very definite answers—answers that occupy a central role in the theory of statistics. A summarization of these fundamental results is as follows:

1. The mean of the theoretical distribution of sample means equals μ, the mean of the parent population.
2. If the variance of the parent population is σ^2, then the variance of the theoretical distribution of the sample means equals σ^2/n, where n is the size of the sample.
3. As the sample size becomes larger and larger, the theo-

retical distribution of the sample means will become closer and closer to a normal distribution, regardless of the shape of the parent population.

These results tell us that by taking larger and larger samples, we can expect the sample mean to come closer and closer to the mean of the parent population. This follows from the fact that the mean of the theoretical sampling distribution of $\bar{x}$ is μ, and its variance becomes smaller as the sample size becomes larger (the variance of the sampling distribution equals σ^2, the parent-population variance, divided by n, the sample size). Furthermore, because we know that the sample means are approximately normally distributed, we actually can calculate the probability that the sample mean will differ from the population mean by more than some given amount.

To illustrate this last point, suppose we take a random sample of size $n = 10$ from the parent population previously described, whose mean is $\mu = 5.5$ and whose variance is $\sigma^2 = 8.25$. Let us find the probability that the sample mean will not exceed 6.5 in value. To solve this problem we can use methods similar to those in Chapter 6, where we calculated areas under a normal curve.

First, we need to find the mean and the standard deviation of the *sampling distribution of the mean*. We know from the foregoing that its mean is the same as that of the parent population, namely, 5.5. We also know from the foregoing that its variance equals the variance of the parent population, *divided by n*. Thus, the required variance is $8.25/10 = 0.825$. Hence, the standard deviation of the sampling distribution is $\sqrt{0.825} = 0.908$.

Next, we standardize; that is, we subtract 5.5 from the value 6.5, and divide the result by 0.908, obtaining

$$z = \frac{6.5 - 5.5}{.908} = 1.10$$

Finally, from Table 12 we find that the area under the standard normal curve to the left of $z = 1.10$ is 0.8643, which gives us our required probability.

We shall now see how these important results apply to the problem of estimating the mean of some population based on the results of a random sample chosen from that population.

Estimating a Population Mean

Any fool can give you an estimate. (In fact, fools are freer with them than wise men.) Very few can tell you whether their estimates will stand up in the light of experience. Statistical inference is based on the philosophy that an estimate is worthless unless it is accompanied by a statement about its reliability.

Whatever method we choose to estimate the mean of a certain population, we would like our estimate to be "reasonably close" to that mean. To explain what is meant by "reasonably close" is not easy. For one thing, the value μ of the population mean is actually unknown; for another, we do not know what results we will get until after we have taken the sample. Thus, we can only ask whether, upon repeated sampling, the sampling distribution of whatever number we calculate from the sample to estimate the sample mean has certain desirable properties.

We know that if we were to employ the sample mean, $\bar{x}$, in estimating μ, its sampling distribution has the mean μ. In other words, we can expect that the means of repeated samples from a given population will center about the mean of that population and not about some other value. For this reason, we say that $\bar{x}$ is an *unbiased estimate* of μ, the mean of the population from which the sample was obtained.

The property of "unbiasedness" is one of the more desirable properties of an estimator. However, there are several ways that we can get an unbiased estimate for μ from the same sample. For instance, the sample median will also give us an unbiased estimate of μ for symmetrically distributed populations. This suggests that we must seek a further criterion for deciding which of several unbiased estimates is "best" for estimating a population mean.

It is not enough for values of an estimate of μ to center about μ on repeated sampling. After all, from any given sample we have only one estimate, and we are not really concerned about others that we might have obtained if we had taken another sample. Although we know that the $\bar{x}$-value at hand comes from a distribution that centers about μ, we would like also to have some knowledge about how far away from μ this value is likely to be.

This is exactly the idea conveyed to us by the notion

of the standard deviation. If the standard deviation (or, equivalently, the variance) of the sampling distribution of the $\bar{x}$-values is small, we can have confidence that any one value of $\bar{x}$ will be close to its mean. In general, among all the various ways of estimating μ, we should like to choose the unbiased estimator that has the smallest variance.

One of the results of the previous section tells us that the variance of the distribution of $\bar{x}$-values is σ^2/n, where σ^2 is the population variance. It is possible to prove that the corresponding sampling distribution of the median has a variance of approximately $1.57(\sigma^2/n)$, 57 percent larger than the variance of the distribution of $\bar{x}$-values. Thus, in any given sample, it is more likely that $\bar{x}$ will be closer to μ than the sample median. This does not imply that the sample mean is *always* closer than the median; in fact, for any given sample we will never have any way of knowing which actually is closer.

It can be shown that in most situations met in actual practice the variance of the sampling distribution of the mean is smaller than that of the sampling distribution of any other unbiased estimator for μ. In other words, in most practical situations, the sample mean is the most acceptable estimate of the population mean μ.

A Confidence Game

When we use the sample mean to estimate the mean of a population, we know that we are using a method that has certain desirable properties; namely $\bar{x}$ is a minimum-variance unbiased estimator for μ. We also know that $\bar{x}$ will rarely, if ever, be exactly equal to μ. Hence, we should want to accompany such an estimate by some statement of how close to the value μ we might reasonably expect this estimate to be.

For large samples (a good rule of thumb is that n should at least equal 30), the sampling distribution of $\bar{x}$ is approximately a normal distribution. But, for a normal distribution, we know that there is approximately a 95 percent chance that the corresponding random variable will lie within two standard deviations on either side of its mean. More specifically, since the variance of $\bar{x}$ is σ^2/n, its standard deviation is $\sigma/\sqrt{n}$; therefore, there is a 95 percent chance that the sample mean will be within $\pm 2\sigma/\sqrt{n}$ units of the population mean μ.

To illustrate, suppose we take a random sample consisting of $n = 100$ observations from some population with unknown mean μ, and the sample mean turns out to be $\bar{x} = 15.8$. Since we do not know σ for the population, we shall estimate it by computing the sample standard deviation, S. If it turns out that $S = 4.6$, we can state with approximately 95 percent assurance that the sample mean will lie within

$$2 \times \frac{4.6}{\sqrt{100}} = 0.92$$

units of the true (but unknown) population mean. In the jargon of statistics: "95 percent confidence limits for μ are 15.8 ± 0.92," or "With 95 percent confidence, μ lies between 14.9 and 16.7."

A pair of numbers, for which we can state with a

given probability that they include the population mean, are called *confidence limits* for μ.

If we wished to be ultraconservative and state confidence limits on the unknown population mean that would be at least 99 percent likely to contain μ, we could have used three-sigma limits. Thus, in the preceding example, our maximum error with approximately 99 percent confidence (actually 99.7 percent) would have been $15.8 \pm 3(4.6/\sqrt{100})$, or 15.8 ± 1.4. On the other hand, if we are satisfied with 90 percent confidence, Table 12 shows that we need to multiply by 1.65, since 90 percent of the area under the normal curve lies within 1.65 standard deviations of the mean. We would then have obtained the 90 percent confidence limits, $15.8 \pm 1.65(4.6/\sqrt{100})$, or 15.8 ± 0.76.

In calculating these confidence limits, we used the sample standard deviation, S, in place of the unknown population standard deviation, σ. This introduces an approximation that readily can be neglected for large samples (n at least equal to 30). For small samples, however, the errors involved in using S in place of σ may not be small. In such cases we cannot use the normal distribution to calculate the required probabilities, as we have just done. Instead, we should have used a distribution known as *Student's t distribution,* which takes into account the additional uncertainty introduced by using S in place of σ. When n equals 30 or more, however, Student's t distribution becomes so close to the standard normal distribution that the errors involved in replacing σ by S are negligible.

Putting It to the Test

Sometimes, rather than *estimate* the value of a parameter, we want to *decide* whether a statement concerning the population mean is true or false. In somewhat more formal language, we wish to *test an hypothesis* about the population mean. For example, we may wish to place an advertisement in a certain magazine only if the mean income of its readers exceeds $10,000 per annum. Based on the results of a random sample chosen from the population of readers, we want to test the hypothesis that the mean annual income of this population exceeds $10,000.

Whenever a decision is based on the results of a random sample, we must face the fact that *errors are unavoidable*. Survey data of incomes of the readers of a magazine might lead us to reject the claim that the mean is an income of at least $10,000, when in fact μ does exceed $10,000. On the other hand, the data might lead us to accept this claim when in fact μ is less than $10,000. The kinds of errors that can be made whenever a decision is taken in the face of uncertainty can be summarized by means of Table 14:

TABLE *14* / *Possible Errors From Accepting or Rejecting Claims Concerning Mean Incomes*

	μ *Is Less Than* $10,000	μ *Is Greater Than* $10,000
Accept the claim	Type II error	No error
Reject the claim	No error	Type I error

A Type I error is committed whenever we falsely reject the claim; a Type II error is committed whenever we falsely accept the claim. In statistical decision-making, our purpose is to control the likelihood that these errors will occur.

Suppose a random sample of 400 readers has a mean annual income of $9,800 and a standard deviation of $2,000. As the sample mean is less than $10,000, we may be tempted to reject the claim that the mean income of the readership is at least $10,000. In so doing, we must recognize the possibility that the true mean income is in fact equal to $10,000, and we were unlucky enough to have selected a sample with a smaller mean. In other words, we should ask the question: "What is the probability of obtaining a sample mean of $9,800 or less from a population whose true mean equals $10,000?"

To answer this question we can make use of the result given on page 111, which allows us to assume that the *sample mean* comes from a distribution that is approximately normal, regardless of the shape of the distribution of incomes from which the mean was calculated. On the hypothesis that this distribution has a mean of $10,000 and a standard deviation of $2,000, the mean of the sampling distribution of $\bar{x}$ also is $10,000, and its standard deviation is $2,000/\sqrt{400}$, or $100. To find the probability that we could have obtained an $\bar{x}$-value of $9,800 or less from such a population, first we standardize, obtaining

$$z = \frac{9,800 - 10,000}{100} = -2.0$$

In other words, $9,800 is two standard deviations below the mean. Referring to Table 12, we compute the probability of obtaining a value less than two standard deviations below the mean to be approximately 2.3 percent.

Because the chance of rejecting the claim—that is, the chance of getting such a small sample mean—is less than 3 percent even when μ equals $10,000, we are on fairly safe ground to reject the claim. This reasoning is fundamental in statistical inference. What we are saying is that we are willing to reject the claim because there is only a very small probability (0.023) that we would have obtained such a result from our sample if the claim were true.

To go one step further, if we are willing to make a Type I error with a probability of 0.05, we can reject the claim whenever the sample mean is $9,835 or less. This statement follows from the fact that

$$z = \frac{9,835 - 10,000}{100} = 1.65$$

and, from Table 12, we observe that a z-value of -1.65 corresponds to a probability of approximately 5 percent—that is, the area under the standard normal curve to the left of -1.65 equals approximately 0.05.

We have developed a decision criterion (the claim is rejected if the mean of a random sample of size 400 is less than $9,835) on the basis of which we can evaluate the claim that the mean income of the magazine readership is at least $10,000. We know that this decision criterion corresponds to a Type I error of approximately 5 percent. But what can be said about the Type

II error? What is the probability that we might accept the claim falsely with the use of this decision criterion?

This is a much more difficult question to answer, because whether we accept the claim depends to a great extent on the actual value of the population mean. If, for example, the population mean equals $10,000, we know that the probability of rejection is 5 percent, and therefore the probability that we will accept the claim is 95 percent.

What would be the chance of accepting the claim if the population mean were $9,900? Our decision criterion states that we will accept whenever $\overline{x}$ is greater than $9,835. Hence, the probability of accepting when μ equals $9,900 can be computed as follows. First, we standardize, obtaining

$$z = \frac{9,835 - 9,900}{100} = -0.65$$

Then, using Table 12 to compute the probability that a standard normal variable will assume a value greater than −0.65, we calculate this probability to be approximately 0.74. In other words, if the population mean were actually equal to $9,900, there would have been a 74 percent chance of accepting the claim.

Proceeding in this way, we could have developed a curve, giving the probability of accepting the claim for various values of the population mean. This curve is shown in Figure 15, and it is called the operating characteristic curve (abbreviated to O.C. curve) of the test. When we examine this O.C. curve, we note that the chance of accepting the claim is at least 0.95 when

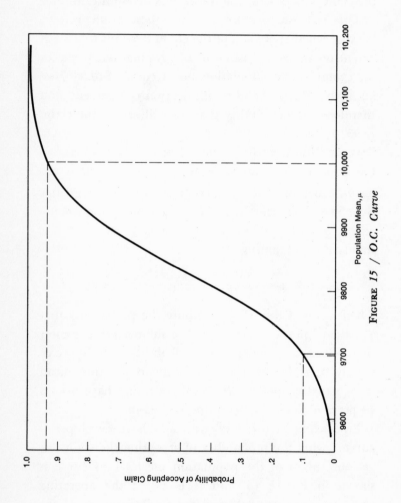

FIGURE 15 / O.C. Curve

the population mean is greater than \$10,000, and it is less than 0.10 when the population mean is less than \$9,710.

By calculating the O.C. curve corresponding to any decision criterion based on the results of a random sample, statisticians can provide the information necessary to evaluate the consequences of applying it. It is important to note that this method does not make the decision—that is still the job of the entrepreneur. Often we can make more than one possible decision in a given situation, and the right decision for us depends on the probability that certain outcomes will be achieved. (Rarely, if ever, can we predict with certainty the outcome of our actions.) This statement is especially true when we base our decision on the results of a random sample (as we often must). For any decision criterion we adopt in such a situation, there corresponds an O.C. curve that gives us the required probabilities. It does not protect us against the possibility of loss, but at least we know the odds against that possibility.

Understanding the Polls

In a large number of surveys, we are interested in the *proportion* of persons who have a certain characteristic. For example, we may be interested in estimating the proportion of potential customers who respond favorably to a certain new product, the proportion of school children whose dietary intake provides them with less than the recommended dietary allotment of vitamin C, or the proportion of the electorate who intend to vote for a certain candidate.

To form an estimate of the desired proportion, we make a certain number, n, of observations and observe the number of times, x, that the appropriate event has occurred. For example, we may question $n = 10,000$ voters and observe that $x = 5,856$ of them intend to vote for a given candidate. The best estimate of the true population proportion is usually the observed relative frequency, x/n, which equals 0.5856 in this example.

We can think of the process of taking such a sample as the performance of a sequence of trials, and with proper random-sampling techniques, these trials will tend to satisfy the assumptions that we stated on page 79, when we derived the binomial distribution. Since the mean of the random variable x having the binomial distribution is $\mu = np$, and its standard deviation is $\sqrt{np(1-p)}$, we can obtain the mean and the standard deviation of the sample proportion of successes, x/n, by dividing these quantities by n. Thus, we obtain

$$\mu_{x/n} = p \quad \text{and} \quad \sigma_{x/n} = \sqrt{\frac{p(1-p)}{n}}$$

When we discussed the normal distribution in Chapter 6, we noted that it arose from the binomial distribution when n, the number of trials, became indefinitely large. Applying this argument in reverse, we observe that the distribution of a random variable having the binomial distribution can be approximated by an appropriately chosen normal distribution whenever n is sufficiently large. Generally speaking, unless the population proportion p is very close to 0 or to 1, this approximation will yield reasonable results whenever the sample size is in excess of 100.

Going one step further, it can be shown that for sufficiently large samples the sample proportion x/n has a sampling distribution that is reasonably well approximated by the normal distribution with the mean p and the standard deviation

$$\sqrt{\frac{p(1-p)}{n}}$$

Using methods analogous to those which allowed us to make statements about the reliability of $\bar{x}$ as an estimate of μ, we can evaluate the sample proportion x/n as an estimate of the population proportion p.

It follows that x/n is an *unbiased* estimate of p, having the standard deviation

$$\sqrt{\frac{p(1-p)}{n}}$$

Thus, we can be approximately 95 percent sure that the interval

$$\frac{x}{n} \pm 2\sqrt{\frac{p(1-p)}{n}}$$

will contain the true proportion, p. In other words, approximate 95 percent confidence limits for p are given by

$$\frac{x}{n} - 2\sqrt{\frac{p(1-p)}{n}} \quad \text{and} \quad \frac{x}{n} + 2\sqrt{\frac{p(1-p)}{n}}$$

To illustrate this point, suppose that a market survey

showed that, of a sample of 1,600 persons interviewed,
360 stated they would like to purchase a certain new
product. Thus, our sample estimate of the true proportion of persons who, in the population from which
the sample was obtained, are willing to purchase this
product is

$$\frac{x}{n} = \frac{360}{1,600} = 0.225$$

To compute the reliability of this estimate, first we
need to calculate its standard deviation. As we have no
way of knowing the value of p, we shall substitute 0.225,
the sample estimate of p, in the formula for the standard
deviation, obtaining

$$\sigma_{x/n} = \sqrt{\frac{p(1 - p)}{n}} = \sqrt{\frac{(.225)(.775)}{1,600}} = 0.010$$

Using two standard deviations for approximately 95
percent confidence, we calculate that confidence limits
for the true proportion p are given by $0.225 \pm .020$, or
$0.205 - 0.245$.

The resulting confidence interval tells us that we have
used a method of sampling that enables us to be 95
percent confident that the true but unknown proportion
of persons desiring to purchase the new product will be
between 0.205 and 0.245. It is a much more satisfying
statement than merely saying, "My estimate of this
proportion is 0.225," because it states how close the
estimate is likely to be to the proportion of persons *in
the population* who favor the product.

It requires large samples to estimate a proportion with
reasonable reliability. If, in the previous example, we

had used a sample of only 100 persons, the standard deviation, instead of being .010, would have become

$$\sqrt{\frac{(.225)(.775)}{100}} = .042$$

and the 95 percent confidence limits would have been 0.225 ± 0.084, or $0.141 - 0.309$, approximately four times as wide as the limits obtained from a sample of size 1,600. In other words, we could not have "pinpointed" the population proportion with a high degree of confidence.

Often it is difficult and expensive to obtain a truly random sample of the large magnitudes required to estimate proportions precisely. Therefore, it is often all too tempting to use "quick and convenient" methods for taking the sample. In so doing we often make the error of neglecting the nonrespondents, who, because they could not be located or refused to cooperate, may well differ in the attribute being measured from those actually included in the sample.

The bias of nonresponse can be extremely serious. For example, in conducting a health survey in which we are attempting to estimate the proportion of persons in a given human population who are suffering from upper respiratory diseases, we may visit a carefully selected sample of households, automatically omitting from our sample those for which there was "nobody home" at the time we called. Since one important reason for this type of nonresponse may well be hospitalization (perhaps for an upper respiratory disease), it is likely that the proportion of persons among the nonrespondents who had an upper respiratory disease is much larger than the proportion of those who did respond. Such a survey could well lead to gross underestimates of the true proportion. Although it may be quite expensive and time-consuming, attempts must be made to subsample the nonrespondents in any survey if the results really are to be believed.

All that we have said so far concerning the reliability of estimates of the population mean or of a population proportion has assumed that the sample was indeed random. If all members of the population under investigation are not given at least a nearly equal chance of being included in the sample, there may be little that can be said about the reliability of the results.

Statisticians have developed special sampling survey methods that allow unequal probabilities for individuals to be included in the sample. These methods have been designed to reduce the costs of making surveys that are intended to meet a fixed level of precision. With careful design, and adherence to statistical principles, surveys making use of "nonconstant probabilities" will yield results with a reliability that can be calculated.

On the other hand, if the survey is conducted in a haphazard manner, so that we have no way of knowing the probability of the inclusion of a given individual in the sample, the results of the survey may bear a closer resemblance to astrology than to statistics. Anyone can give you estimates or tell you what decisions to make; the man who deserves your attention is the one who also can tell you the reliability of his estimates or the magnitude of the possible errors involved in the recommended decisions.

Bayesian Inference—Use of Prior Information

In many situations it is best to consider collateral as well as direct information in making decisions. To illustrate, suppose you receive components from two different vendors for use in assembling a finished product. The first vendor supplies 75 percent of the components, and the second supplies the remaining 25 percent. The percentage of defectives among those components supplied by the first vendor is known to be 2 percent; for the second vendor it is 4 percent.

A lot consisting of a large number of these components is discovered in the warehouse without the tag identifying the vendor who supplied it. In order to estimate the proportion of defectives in this lot, it was decided to take a small sample. Accordingly, 10 components were selected from the lot at random, and it was discovered that 1 was defective. Using this information, together with the collateral information about our two vendors' past performance, we would like to estimate the true proportion of defective components in the lot.

If the lot had been supplied by the first vendor, whose relative frequency of defectives is known to be 2 percent, then the probability that, of 10 components, 1 would have been defective is given by the binomial distribution to be

$$\binom{10}{1} (.02)^1(.98)^9 = 0.167$$

Likewise, the probability that, if the lot had been supplied by the second vendor, 1 out of 10 would have been defective is given by

$$\binom{10}{1} (.04)^1(.96)^9 = 0.277$$

Thus, if the lot came from Vendor 1, we would have observed the given result (1 failure out of 10) with a probability of only 0.167; on the other hand, this probability would have increased to 0.277 if the lot came from Vendor 2.

Since we purchase 75 percent of these components from Vendor 1, we could have guessed that there is a 75 percent chance that the unmarked lot came from this vendor. But, this *prior probability* needs to be modified in the light of the sample evidence, as it now seems somewhat more likely our sample was obtained from Vendor 2. The situation is now as described in the tree shown in Figure 16.

If we use the formula for Bayes' rule (page 71), we obtain

P (Vendor 1 | 1 defective out of 10)

$$= \frac{.75 \times .167}{(.75 \times .167) + (.25)(.277)}$$

$$= 0.644$$

It therefore follows that

P (Vendor 2 | 1 defective out of 10)
$$= 1 - P \text{ (Vendor 1 | 1 defective out of 10)} = 0.356$$

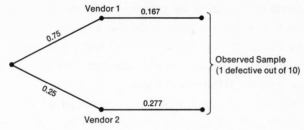

FIGURE *16* / *"Tree" for Bayesian Inference*

We thus have the following probability distribution for p, the proportion of defectives in the lot:

p	Probability
.02 (Vendor 1)	.644
.04 (Vendor 2)	.356

The mean of this distribution is given by $(.02 \times .644) + (.04 \times .356) = 0.27$. This figure furnishes us with a *Bayesian estimate* of the proportion of defectives in the lot.

Here is an example of a situation in which the methods for estimating proportions described in the preceding section are of little help, because the sample size is small (only 10 components were tested). However, there is at least an intuitive feeling that some prior information might be helpful. Since 75 percent of lots come from Vendor 1, we are strongly predisposed to tag the lot in question "Vendor 1." However, the sample result (1 failure out of 10) makes it appear more likely that the lot should have been tagged "Vendor 2." We resolved this conflict by making a Bayesian inference, using Bayes' Rule to compute the *a posteriori* probabilities that these vendors supplied the lot in question, and basing on these probabilities our estimate of the proportion of defectives in the lot.

The use of estimates of prior probabilities to make Bayesian inferences of the type described has lately received much attention. This method was derived primarily with business and economic applications in mind, because in such problems there is rarely sufficient sampling information available on which to base an intelligent decision.

CHAPTER 8

The Numbers Game

A special kind of average, one to which increasing economic importance has been attached, is an *index number*. Such numbers are used primarily to tell how much one quantity has changed relative to another. Thus, if a man paid $12 for a pair of shoes in 1950 and $15 for a pair of like quality in 1960, we would say that an index of the change in the price of shoes over the 10-year period 1950–1960 is $15/12 = 1.25$ or, expressed as a percentage, that the index equals 125. This number is a primitive example of a price index; as it involves a simple ratio of two prices, it is called a *price relative*.

In its most rudimentary form, an index number involves a simple *binary comparison*, a comparison between two prices or quantities. Economists have not been able to resist the temptation, however, to generalize this idea in two main directions. These generalizations broaden the scope and applicability of index numbers, and each carries its own problems of computation and interpretation.

One generalization involves the use of *comparisons in series*. Such comparisons involve the generation of a sequence of binary index numbers, usually in the form of a time series. For example, suppose we wish to make a comparison in series of business expenditures for new plant and equipment based on the information in Table 15.

TABLE 15 / *Comparison of Business Expenditures for New Plant and Equipment*

Year	Business Expenditures for New Plant and Equipment (Billions of Dollars)	Index (1962 = 100)
1962	37.31	100
1963	39.22	105
1964	44.90	120
1965	51.96	139
1966	60.23	161

SOURCE: Extracted from U.S. Bureau of the Census, *Statistical Abstract of the United States: 1966*, 87th ed. (Washington, D.C., 1966), p. 499.

One method that can be used involves the selection of a *base period* and a comparison of values for all other periods to the value during the base period. Suppose we select the year 1962 as the base period; then the index for the year 1963 is

$$(39.22/37.31)100 = 105$$

Values of the index thus computed for the years 1964, 1965, and 1966 also are shown in the table.

One of the problems constantly plaguing economists who are constructing indexes is the choice of the base period. Generally speaking, the following guidelines are useful. First, because comparisons over a great period of time tend to lose their meaning, the base period is generally chosen in the relatively recent past. Second, in order to avoid misleading comparisons, economists generally try to choose a period of relative economic stability. In any event, the choice of a base period is somewhat arbitrary and, as you can readily see, the value of the index for any other period is dependent upon this choice.

A second generalization involves the inclusion of more than one item for comparison. The usefulness of an index relating the price of shoes to some base year is severely limited. A broader comparison involving prices paid by the consumer for a number of different items would be far more appealing. But the moment we attempt to expand an index to include more than one item, we are confronted by several serious problems. Which items shall we choose, and what interpretation should we give the resulting index? Having decided on a choice of items to be included, how shall we combine their individual prices or quantities in the construction of a meaningful index?

The broader our objective, the more difficult the decision as to which items we should include. If we wished merely to construct an index reflecting changes in the price of "men's footwear," the task would be simpler than if we were interested in constructing a "consumer-price index." Even in the case of men's footwear there are problems that may be extremely difficult to solve. It would seem fairly clear that we should include shoes, slippers, boots, rubbers, galoshes, shoelaces, and socks. But should we also include such items as garters and spats? These items are essentially relics of the past, but if we chose 1925 as our base year they would have made up a not inconsequential portion of the market for men's footwear. To complicate matters further, we have no guarantee that they might not come into vogue again within the next few years.

In constructing a more general consumer-price index, this problem has to be faced many times. For example, television sets are a commonly purchased consumer item today, but as late as 1945 they were virtually unknown. There is no telling what new and as yet unheard-of inventions will make important inroads into the consumer's pocketbook tomorrow.

The problem of combining the prices or quantities of the individual items comprising an index is equally fraught with difficulties. The value or quantity of each item must somehow be *weighted* to reflect its relative importance to the whole. The need for weights is exemplified by the case of the cook who claims that his beef-and-rabbit stew consists of equal parts of each: one cow and one rabbit.

Selection of Index Items

The choice of which items should comprise an index should be determined by the purpose for which the index is intended. An index of production for the primary metals industries requires a list of all metals produced by each company in the field and the production quantity of each for the specified period of time. A more ambitious "index of industrial production" would require similar lists for each industry in the United States.

The task of compiling a list of these industries, let alone listing their individual products, is a difficult one. It is constantly necessary to make somewhat arbitrary decisions. For example, where does one draw the line between "chemical products" and "petroleum and coal products"? Are vitamin supplements "food and beverage products" or "pharmaceuticals"?

To construct, for example, an index of prices that farmers receive for their products, an enormous data-collection program must be organized. The Department of Agriculture currently collects monthly price information for about 125 farm commodities and annual data on nearly 100 additional commodities. In addition, it collects prices paid by farmers for almost 400 items, including food, clothing, machinery, equipment, and so forth. These prices form the basis of an index of prices paid by farmers. The ratio of the index of prices received to the index of prices paid is called the *parity ratio*, and it is a major factor in congressional decisions involving farm programs.

To construct an index of department store sales, monthly sales reports are obtained from 1,550 stores. The problem of defining exactly what is a "department store" as opposed to a "specialty store" or a "discount house" is one that probably never will be solved to everyone's satisfaction.

Seemingly one of the simplest areas in which to solve the problem of which items to include in an index would be the stock market. For a given stock exchange such as the New York Stock Exchange or the American Stock Exchange, there is a long but definitely limited list of issues traded. But some are common stocks, some are preferred stocks, some are warrants; some trade actively, some sporadically; some involve high volume, some low volume; and so forth. In all likelihood, there are nearly as many opinions about which to exclude and which to include as there are issues.

Nevertheless, such indexes are constructed, which means that somewhere enough compromises were made concerning which items should be included and which excluded to allow the work to proceed. Much of the time these decisions are made on the basis of availability of data. For every item to be included in an index there must exist some method of regularly obtaining accurate information about its price or cost and its quantity.

Such information is obtained in several ways. For short periods—weekly, monthly, or quarterly—a sample often is taken. Sometimes it is a random sample, sometimes a "judgment sample." Always there is some difficulty in delineating the population (the specific stores, industries, farms, etc.) from which the sample is derived. In addition, periodic information is not always obtained for every item on the list. Sometimes the value corresponding to certain items not included in the sample is imputed from the values of others that have been included.

These figures are usually "backed up" by more complete surveys, or even the results of the latest United States census. Figures provided by the U.S. Bureau of the Census may be used to "blow up" the sample information to represent the entire United States economy. There is a constant struggle to insure that the prices and quantities that make up a given index do not lag the reporting period or are not otherwise distorted by basic trends in the economy.

Weighted Averages

As defined in Chapter 3, the mean of a set of observations is calculated simply by adding the individual items of data and dividing by the total number of items. In so doing, we actually assign equal weights to each number making up the mean. In that chapter we briefly discussed a generalization, called the weighted mean, and applied it to the problem of finding the mean of several groups of observations whose group means were known. Here, we extend this concept for the purpose of applying it to the construction of index numbers.

Suppose we wanted to calculate the average price received by farmers for poultry in 1965, and we had the information given in Table 16. Reasoning that the farmer received an average price of $1.17 per head for chickens, $0.34 per dozen for eggs, and $4.39 per head for turkeys, we would find nothing mathematically

TABLE *16* / *Poultry on U.S. Farms—1965*

CHICKENS		EGGS		TURKEYS	
Number Jan. 1	Value per Head	Millions of Dozens	Price per Dozen	Number Jan. 1	Value per Head
375,424,000	$1.17	5,379	$0.34	6,421,000	$4.39

SOURCE: Extracted from U.S. Bureau of the Census, *Statistical Abstract of the United States: 1966,* 87th ed. (Washington, D.C., 1966), p. 670.

wrong if we had computed the average of these three items

$$\frac{1.17 + 0.34 + 4.39}{3} = \$1.97$$

interpreting the result as the average price for poultry and poultry products received by farmers in the United States during 1965.

This average fails to take into account that, whereas over 5 billion dozens of eggs were produced in 1965, less than 400 million chickens and little more than 6 million turkeys were produced. To reflect these quantity differences, we could have weighted each price mean by the corresponding quantity to produce the following kind of weighted average:

$$\frac{375,424,000 \times 1.17 + 5,379,000,000 \times 0.34 + 6,421,000 \times 4.39}{375,424,000 + 5,379,000,000 + 6,421,000}$$

$$= 0.40$$

Equivalently, we could have observed that, of all the poultry products produced, approximately 6.5 percent were chickens, 93.4 percent were eggs (in dozens), and 0.1 percent were turkeys. The weighted average price per unit of poultry production received by farmers in 1965 would then have been calculated as follows:

$$\frac{6.5 \times 1.17 + 93.4 \times 0.34 + 0.1 \times 4.39}{100.0} = 0.40$$

Note that we obtain the same result with either interpretation. However, this result is very different indeed from the less meaningful if simpler unweighted average.

This weighted average price of $.40 no longer has a straightforward interpretation. There is no poultry product for which the farmer received an average price of $.40 during 1965. The figure $.40 merely reflects the total price received by farmers for *all units* produced in 1965, divided by the total number of units produced.

The choice of weights to be used in the construction of any economic index is a difficult one. Generally speaking, the weights should reflect the relative importance of the various items included. If a price index is to be constructed, it is customary to weight the price of each item by the corresponding quantity, as we did in constructing a weighted average poultry price for 1965. On the other hand, if we are constructing an index of quantities, the weights usually are chosen to be corresponding prices or other indicators of relative value.

Even if there were general agreement that the weights to be used in constructing a price index should be the corresponding quantities, there still would be some unresolved difficulties. In constructing a binary index, comparing the weighted average price for a given year to the weighted average price for a base year, which quantities should we use? Should the weights correspond to quantities in the base year, to quantities in the given year, or to quantities in some other period?

In the construction of most indexes a maximum amount of information concerning the base year is generally available. (Many times the base year is chosen for this reason, or, once the base year is selected, extensive statistics are gathered for that year.) Thus, for convenience, base-year quantities often are used as weights in economic indexes. Such weights, however, do not reflect the changing composition of the "market basket" (the list of items included in the index). There is a general tendency for quantities to increase relative to one another, corresponding to items whose prices have decreased, and to decrease relative to one another, corresponding to items whose prices have increased. Therefore, such an index will tend to have an upward bias, that is, to somewhat overestimate increases in prices.

On the other hand, if the weights are chosen to reflect quantities during the current year, the resulting index will somewhat underestimate increases in prices; that is, it will tend to have a downward bias. An approximate solution to this problem consists of computing the index both ways and averaging the results. Of course the resulting value becomes even more difficult to interpret, and the extra labor required to obtain both sets of weights tends severely to restrict the use of this method in practice.

A somewhat more practical way to get around this

problem is to use weights that refer to some period other than either the base year or the given year. The advantage here is that the base period later can be changed without the necessity of making corresponding changes in the weights. Also, unlike the use of given-year weights, there is no need to calculate the weights anew each year.

Generally speaking, the selection of appropriate weights for most indexes requires a considerable amount of both judgment and labor. Whatever the choice of method to assign weights, the resulting index will be a somewhat arbitrary idealization of the quantity that it purports to measure.

Construction of Index Numbers

In the following discussion we shall confine ourselves to price indexes that have quantity weights. There is no essential difference between the ideas of economic indexes illustrated in this context and the equivalent ideas for quantity indexes that have price weights.

To illustrate the calculation of price indexes, let us

TABLE *17* / *Livestock—Average Chicago Market Price*
(Dollars per 100 Pounds—Live Weight)

	1955	1965
Beef cattle	22.59	25.81
Calves	24.80	29.00
Sheep	5.18	6.42
Lambs	20.95	24.29
Hogs	14.80	20.78

SOURCE: Extracted from U.S. Bureau of the Census, *Statistical Abstract of the United States: 1966*, 87th ed. (Washington, D.C., 1966), p. 669.

refer to Table 17, which shows livestock prices at the Chicago market.

To construct a *simple unweighted index* comparing livestock prices in 1965 and in 1955, we have only to add the 1965 prices and divide their sum by the sum of the 1955 prices. We obtain

$$I = \frac{25.81 + 29.00 + 6.42 + 24.29 + 20.78}{22.59 + 24.80 + 5.18 + 20.95 + 14.80} = \frac{106.30}{88.32} = 1.20$$

It is customary to multiply the resulting index by 100, obtaining 120, so that it is expressed as a percentage. This result tells us that the average livestock price in 1965 was 120 percent of the 1955 price; in other words, these prices increased by 20 percent during the 10-year period.

In computing this index we made use of prices that were expressed in dollars per hundredweight. If, for some reason, the price of beef cattle were expressed in dollars per pound (so that the 1965 price would be quoted as 26 cents instead of $25.81), the value of the index would have changed. To avoid this kind of problem, we could have computed a separate index for each category of livestock and then averaged the resulting ratios. If we do this, the index for beef cattle becomes $(25.81/22.59)100 = 114$, and we would have obtained the same value regardless of whether the price were expressed in dollars per pound or in dollars per hundredweight. Repeating this calculation for the remaining four categories of livestock, and averaging the *price relatives* so obtained, we obtain the following index value:

$$I = \frac{114 + 117 + 124 + 116 + 140}{5} = 122$$

called the *arithmetic mean of price relatives*. Note that its value differs somewhat from that of the simple unweighted index.

The unweighted index numbers so calculated have the perfectly acceptable interpretation that they represent the average percentage of 1965 market prices compared to 1955 prices, *per classification of livestock*. They do not, however, reflect prices paid for livestock as a single category, because equal quantities of each category are not normally offered for sale.

Suppose we were instead to construct a weighted index, using as weights the percentages of each category of livestock sold in 1955 given in Table 18.

TABLE *18* / *Livestock Sold in 1955*

Category	% Sold
Beef cattle	12
Calves	6
Sheep	28
Lambs	2
Hogs	52
	100

SOURCE: Extracted from U.S. Bureau of the Census, *Statistical Abstract of the United States: 1966*, 87th ed. (Washington, D.C., 1966), p. 669.

The weighted mean price paid for livestock in 1955 would now equal

$$\frac{12 \times 22.59 + 6 \times 24.80 + 28 \times 5.18 + 2 \times 20.95 + 52 \times 14.80}{100}$$

$$= 13.76$$

for 1965 it would equal

$$\frac{12 \times 25.81 + 6 \times 29.00 + 28 \times 6.42 + 2 \times 24.29 + 52 \times 20.78}{100}$$

$$= 17.93$$

Thus, the *weighted price index*, where the weights come from the base year (1955), is given by

$$I = (17.93/13.76)100 = 130$$

Note that this value is considerably higher than 120, the value of the simple unweighted price index. The reason for this difference becomes apparent when we observe that the price of hogs increased by 40 percent from 1955 to 1965, and hogs constitute 52 percent of the "product mix" in the livestock area.

Using the same weights, we could have constructed a *weighted mean of price relatives*, as follows:

$$I = \frac{12 \times 114 + 6 \times 117 + 28 \times 124 + 2 \times 116 + 52 \times 140}{100}$$

$$= 131$$

Perhaps the index with the most important and widespread economic and political implications is the so-called "consumer price index" prepared by the Bureau of Labor Statistics. This index is computed monthly, based on a "market basket" list of items gathered periodically in urban areas throughout the country. It is a weighted price index whose weights are based on some period other than the base period or the given year.

The method used for computing this index is somewhat different from the methods that we have heretofore illustrated. Instead of dividing by the sum of the weighted prices for some base period, the index is computed in a chainwise fashion. The numerator is the weighted sum of prices for a given period, and the denominator is the weighted sum of prices *for the immediately preceding period*. Such a *chain index* has the advantage of permitting the introduction of new commodities or the deletion of old ones without the need to recalculate the previous values of the index. Also, it is a relatively simple matter to adjust the weights whenever such an adjustment is indicated.

A chain index also has the following important property. If I_1 stands for the value of such an index representing the change from the immediately preceding period to the present period, and I_2 represents the value of the index corresponding to the change in the preceding period from the next preceding one, then the product $I_1/100 \times I_2/100 \times 100$ will be an index of the relative change over the entire interval of two periods. For example, if for July of some year the consumer price index takes on the value 101, meaning a 1 percent price increase from June, and if the August index is 102, meaning a further 2 percent increase over July, then the index representing the price change from June to August will equal $1.01 \times 1.02 \times 100$, or 103.

This discussion shows us that we should use great care in the interpretation of index numbers. The more general an index number becomes, the less direct is its connection with the real economic world. After all, an index number is only a single value, a kind of a weighted mean, used to describe a highly complex and many-faceted economic phenomenon.

Since many important economic and political decisions are made on the basis of values of series of index numbers, economists and businessmen should be doubly sure to understand how they are constructed, what decisions and assumptions went into their formulation, and what economic phenomena they are attempting to describe. Most of all, they should remember that by constructing an index number we are imposing a heavy burden on a single number. When we observe how many different values—some directly observed, some estimated on the basis of a sample, and some arrived at by a judgmental process—have been condensed to produce a single number on which the salaries of many workers depend, we stand somewhat in awe of the entire process.

As long as we understand that we are playing a "numbers game" and are willing to abide by the consequences of the somewhat arbitrary decisions that went into the construction of our economic indicators, these indicators should not prove too burdensome. As long as we keep a wary eye out for the exceptional case, understanding both the strengths and the weaknesses of economic indexes, we can avoid their major pitfalls.

CHAPTER 9

The Crystal Ball

We study the past so that we may better predict the future. Economic statistics necessarily are compilations of past events over which we no longer have any control. Their real value lies in their usefulness in controlling the current economy and in predicting its future. But, as anyone who has ever bought a share of stock or begun a new business venture well knows, predicting the future of the economy, either in the small or in the large, can be a very risky business.

We have a certain amount of faith in economic predictions because we observe that all the myriad observations that are made on our economy are somehow related. Economic indicators normally vary in relationship to each other, with at least a roughly predictable rhythm, and they seem to change with time according to some general laws, however poorly understood.

Statistical science provides several imperfect but increasingly useful tools for studying patterns of variation and covariation of economic observations. In this chapter we shall introduce some of the more widely used methods comprising this somewhat crude arsenal of weapons against the future.

Fitting a Line

The values of the Gross National Product and the Index of Industrial Production are shown for the 25 years from 1929–1953 in Table 19. A study of this table shows that these values are related. They seem to be following the same general upward trend, and both series seem to follow the same general peaks and troughs.

Is it possible to construct a measure of the strength of the relationship between these two series? In what way could such a measure help us to predict the value of the Industrial Production Index that might correspond to some future value of the Gross National Product?

The strength of the relationship between these two series becomes more evident if we graph them, not as individual series fluctuating together with time, but as pairs of values tied together by the common bond of time. In Figure 17, we have plotted the value of the Gross National Product on the horizontal axis, and the corresponding Industrial Production Index on the vertical axis. Each point on the graph represents the *paired*

TABLE *19* / *Relationship Between GNP and Industrial Production*

Year	Gross National Product (Billions of [1939] Dollars)	Index of Industrial Production (1947–1949 = 100)
1929	86	59
1930	78	49
1931	72	40
1932	62	31
1933	61	37
1934	68	40
1935	74	47
1936	84	56
1937	88	61
1938	84	48
1939	91	58
1940	100	67
1941	115	87
1942	130	106
1943	146	127
1944	157	125
1945	153	107
1946	138	90
1947	139	100
1948	144	104
1949	144	97
1950	156	112
1951	167	120
1952	172	124
1953	179	134

values of these two economic indicators for a *given year.*

A glance at this graph (sometimes called a *scatter diagram*) shows that a very strong relationship does indeed link these two measures. But, of at least equal importance, the relationship appears to be linear; that is, there appears to be a constant proportional relationship between industrial production and the GNP.

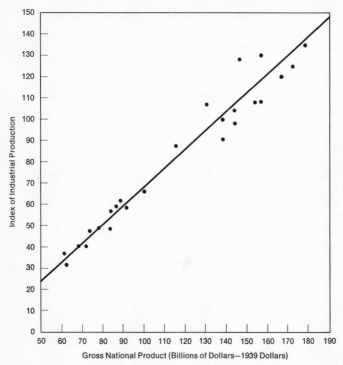

FIGURE *17 / Relationship Between GNP and Industrial Production*

Suppose we go one step farther and ask for the value of that proportion. More precisely, we wish to know how much of a change in the Index of Industrial Production we could expect to correspond to a unit change in the GNP. This question can best be answered if we find the straight line that best fits the data graphed in Figure 17.

The equation of a straight line can be written in the form

$$y = a + bx$$

In this form, x is called the *independent variable,* and its values are plotted with reference to the horizontal axis ("x-axis"); y is called the *dependent variable,* and its values are plotted with reference to the vertical axis ("y-axis"). The constant a is called the *intercept* of the line; it is the value of y that occurs when $x = 0$. The constant b is called the *slope* of the line; its value tells us the magnitude of the change in y that results from an increase in x of one unit. If b is positive, y *increases* as x increases; if b is negative, y *decreases* as x increases. If $b = 0$, the value of y *does not change* as x changes.

There appears to be no obvious guide to finding the "best-fitting" straight line. Mathematicians concerned with the general problem of fitting lines and curves to somewhat scattered data have developed a very satisfying criterion, called the "criterion of least squares." It turns out that some very desirable statistical properties obtain in the estimate of the slope of the line—the increase in industrial production corresponding to a unit increase in the GNP—derived from the least-squares method. Under a somewhat technical but highly plausible set of assumptions, it provides that unbiased estimator of the "true" slope that has minimum variance.

How do we find the best fitting line according to the criterion of least squares? The following is a useful mnemonic device if you have a desk calculator handy. First, write down the equation of a straight line, leaving spaces, as follows:

$$y = a \quad + b \quad x$$

Then, multiply everything by x, and write

$$xy = a \quad x + b \quad x^2$$

Now, put a summation sign (Σ) in front of each term in the equations. This sign tells us to add all values of the quantity it precedes. For example, Σy means "Add the n values of y." We thus obtain

$$\Sigma y = an + b\Sigma x$$

$$\Sigma xy = a\Sigma x + b\Sigma x^2$$

(the sum of n terms of the constant a is an).

These equations are the so-called "normal equations" for fitting a straight line. In our example, we shall let x represent a value of the GNP (in billions of dollars) and y represent the corresponding value of the production index. In other words, we are taking the production index to be our dependent variable, and we shall predict its value based on the value of the independent variable, GNP. The symbol n simply represents the total number of data points (years, in our case) and here it equals 25. The normal equations tell us that we must calculate the sum of the 25 GNP values, Σx, the sum of the squares of the GNP values, Σx^2, the sum of the production-index values, Σy, and the sum of the products of each GNP value, multiplied by the corresponding production-index value, Σxy.

With the aid of our desk calculator, we get

$$\Sigma x = 2{,}888 \qquad \Sigma y = 2{,}026$$
$$\Sigma x^2 = 369{,}652 \qquad \Sigma xy = 264{,}648$$

If we substitute these results into the normal equations, they become a bit less formidable looking:

$$2,026 = 25a + 2,888b$$
$$264,648 = 2,888a + 369,652b$$

Now, all we have to do is solve this set of simultaneous linear equations. You can check by substitution that $a = -17.08$ and $b = 0.85$. This result ($b = 0.85$) tells us that for every billion-dollar increase in the GNP, the Index of Industrial Production can be expected to increase by 0.85. The negative intercept ($a = -17.08$) indicates that the production index would be negative if the GNP were equal to zero. This seemingly spurious result could have resulted from a lack of linearity in the relationship for very small values of the GNP, or it could mean that no industrial production could be expected from an economy with a small GNP.

The equation of the best-fitting straight line is

$$y = -17.08 + 0.85x$$

This line is shown in Figure 17 along with the original data points, and it appears to provide a "good fit" to these points. To graph the line, we simply found two convenient points on it ($x = 50$, corresponding to $y = -17.08 + 0.85 \times 50 = 25.4$; and $x = 200$, corresponding to $y = -17.08 + 0.85 \times 200 = 152.9$) and connected them with a straight line.

If we wish to use this line for prediction, we can do so in the following way. To predict the value of y when $x = 120$, we substitute 120 for x in the equation $y = -17.08 + 0.85x$, obtaining $y = 84.9$. To predict the

value of the Index of Industrial Production if the
GNP reaches 300, we similarly obtain $y = -17.08 + (0.85 \times 300) = 237.9$.

How good are these predictions? First, they can be
no better than our assumption that the "true" underlying relationship between x and y is linear. However,
even if it is slightly curved, our prediction that $y = 84.9$ when $x = 120$ should be much closer to fact than
our prediction that $y = 237.9$ when $x = 300$. This fol-
lows from the fact that $x = 120$ lies near the center of
the observations, where slight departures from linearity
in the underlying relationship will not be too serious.
However, if the real (but unknown) relationship is
curved, our prediction that $y = 237.9$ when $x = 300$
could be considerably in error. Thus, the validity of
any *extrapolated* prediction (as opposed to the *inter-
polation* for $x = 120$) is strongly dependent on the
truth of the assumption that the relationship is truly
linear.

Correlation

Let us accept for the moment the assumption that
the relationship between two economic indicators, x
and y, is linear. Hence, it is assumed that we can express
y in terms of x by means of an equation of the form
$y = a + bx$. This equation exhibits the *mathematical
model* upon which we shall base our predictions. Although it may seem unwise to base economic predictions on an assumption, let us remember that no predictions of any kind would ever be possible without some

kind of underlying model. The "laws of physics" are nothing more than mathematical models that explicitly state the assumptions, empirically tested, upon which the physicist bases his predictions concerning the behavior of the physical world.

Given this assumption, can we measure the strength of the linear relationship between x and y? To construct such a measure, again let us make use of the statistical idea of the variance. Before we fitted the line, the values of y (the production index) varied from 31 to 134; and, without taking into account the corresponding value of x, we would have found it difficult to predict what value of y to expect in any given year. The variance of these y-values can be calculated by using the computing formula for the variance described on page 44, and we obtain

$$S_y = \frac{(25)(191{,}244) - (2026)^2}{(25)(24)}$$
$$= 710.7$$

This figure gives us a measure of the variability of the y-values prior to fitting the line.

Now let us determine the reduction in variance when we take into account the relationship between x and y. Suppose, instead of finding the mean-squared deviation of the y-values from their *mean* (which is exactly what we did when we calculated $S_y{}^2$), we now calculate the mean-squared deviation of the y-values from the *predicted values*. Since the predicted value of y is $a + bx$, this is equivalent to finding the mean-squared deviation of the y-values from the best-fitting straight line, or the mean of the quantities.

$$[y - (a + bx)]^2$$

To find the mean, we add these squared deviations, but we now divide by $n - 2$ (instead of $n - 1$, as in the case of S_y^2) because we had to estimate *two* constants (a and b) instead of just one ($\bar{y}$). We shall use the symbol S_e^2 to represent the resulting quantity.

If we perform this somewhat lengthy calculation, we get $S_e^2 = 44.6$, and we shall refer to this quantity as the *residual variance*; it is a measure related to the variability of prediction.

Note that the *original* variance was $S_y^2 = 710.7$ and the *residual* variance was $S_e^2 = 44.6$; therefore, the *reduction* in variability achieved by the linear relationship of y to x is $S_y^2 - S_e^2 = 666.1$. Now we shall compare this reduction to the original variance by calculating the ratio

$$r^2 = \frac{S_y^2 - S_e^2}{S_y^2} = \frac{666.1}{710.7} = 0.94$$

This final calculation shows that we achieved a 94 percent reduction in variance by predicting y on the basis of x. This quantity (r^2) is called the *coefficient of determination*. If the data points lie exactly on a straight line, its value will be 1 (since S_e^2 will equal 0). On the other hand, if the points were so scattered that a straight line provides no better predictive power than $\bar{y}$ itself, S_e^2 will equal S_y^2, and r^2 will equal zero. The closer the value of the coefficient of determination to 1, the better the predictive power of the linear relationship.

It is customary in some applications to take the square

root of the coefficient of determination, that is, to compute

$$r = \pm\sqrt{\frac{S_y{}^2 - S_e{}^2}{S_e{}^2}}$$

taking the positive sign if b, the slope of the line, is positive (the line slopes upward) and the negative sign if the slope is negative (the line slopes downward). The resulting number is called the *coefficient of linear correlation* of x and y, or simply the *correlation*. A positive correlation indicates that y *increases* as x increases; a negative correlation indicates that y *decreases* as x increases.

The correlation coefficient is another of those frequently computed and often misinterpreted statistics. It is tempting to act as if two series were *causally* related whenever their correlation is close to $+1$ or to -1, and to act as if they were entirely unrelated if their correlation is close to 0 in value. Either of these conclusions can be false.

The world abounds with "nonsense correlations." For example, if we were to correlate, for the period 1946–1966, the series giving teachers' median salaries with the series giving annual expenditures on alcoholic-beverage consumption, we would find a very high positive correlation. This is a fact; but it probably is not a fact that the relationship is causal. Only in our cups would we conclude, "Sure, you give a teacher a raise and he goes out and buys more booze."

Why, then, are these two series correlated? The answer lies in *concomitant variation*: There is a third variable (probably related both to increases in real disposable personal income and to inflation) to which both teachers' salaries and alcohol consumption are causally related. As the nation becomes more prosperous, it drinks more liquor, and (as if to salve its conscience) it also pays its teachers better.

We have observed that, if two series are strongly correlated, they may not be causally related. However, if they are correlated, and if any concomitant variable that links them together continues to operate in the future as it has in the past, the value of one economic measure nevertheless is useful in predicting the other. Where the chain of causality is weakest, however, so are the resulting predictions. If the force of any concomitant variation changes, without our understanding the nature or existence of such changes, the resulting predictions can be drastically in error.

Economic Time Series

So far in this chapter we have given a rudimentary introduction to modern methods of prediction that could come under the heading "econometric methods." We have discussed how econometricians remove the factor of "time" and directly study the relationship between two series.

Econometricians also study relationships among several series, with the aid of modern high-speed computing methods. In so doing they make use of what is known as "multivariate statistical analysis," in which relationships among a large number of economic variables can be considered simultaneously. These methods are primarily mathematical, and modern students of economic theory and econometrics find that their preparation must include liberal doses of calculus and advanced statistical theory. Although econometrics is a young science, it promises to make important advances in economic forecasting, which some economists believe to be the raison d'être of economics.

The traditional approach to economic forecasting consists of directly observing the behavior with time of an economic index or other measure. Sometimes a graph of the resulting "time series" is all that is required to grasp the general behavior of the given index in the past and to make gross generalizations about its behavior in the future.

Economic time series, however, often can be difficult to understand and interpret. Business cycles, seasonal variations, and an irregular or "random" pattern of unpredictable variability (caused by such unforeseeable events as bad weather, strikes, new products) can easily mask long-term trends. Traditionally, time-series analysis attempts to isolate each of these components and to estimate separately its contribution to the entire series. For this purpose, statisticians customarily regard a time series as being composed of the following components:

1. Trends
   a. Secular trends
   b. Business cycles

2. Seasonal Variations
3. Irregular Variations

Before we can begin the analysis of a time series, however, we must often make certain minor, but nonetheless important, adjustments. These adjustments are necessary because of irregularities in the calendar and, in the case of a price index or value variable, changes in the "value of the dollar." For example, department store sales might appear to have decreased in February; however, this apparent decrease may be explained simply by the fact that February has 28 days. To remove artifacts in time series arising from irregularities in the calendar, monthly figures are divided by the total number of business days in the month to produce an average daily figure for the month; then they are multiplied by the length of an "average month" (approximately 30.4 days in years other than leap years). In certain cases a value series also may be "deflated" to reflect "constant dollars."

Once these initial adjustments have been made, we wish to eliminate seasonal and irregular variations, in an effort to estimate the long-term trend. Whether this trend should include or exclude the "business cycle," and whether it is even possible to separate the trend from the business cycle, are matters of much dispute among economic forecasters. Proposed solutions to this problem are both complicated and controversial. Therefore, we shall dodge the issue by simply referring to "the trend" and leaving it to the reader's own personal taste as to whether or not it should include any business cycle.

There are several methods for isolating the trend, that is, for eliminating seasonal and irregular variations from a time series. The problem of "smoothing" an economic time series has received much attention in the past, and a bewildering variety of "solutions" have been offered.

Among the simpler methods are the method of moving averages and the method of regression. To detrend a time series by means of the method of moving averages, we simply replace the value of the series corresponding to a given month by the average of the values for that month and several adjacent months. For example, a five-month moving average would replace each value in the time series by the average of the values for that month, the two preceding months, and the two succeeding months. The number of months (or weeks, etc.) used in constructing a moving average is called the *period* of the moving average. If this period is equal to that of the seasonal cycle, or some multiple of it, the technique will remove seasonal variations. For this reason, quarterly, semiannual, and 12-month moving averages are frequently used.

If we think of irregular variations as representing the values of some random variable superimposed on the time series, having the variance σ^2, we observe that the process of taking a moving average reduces their effect. If the moving average is of period n (consists of averages over n months), the variance of the mean—that is,

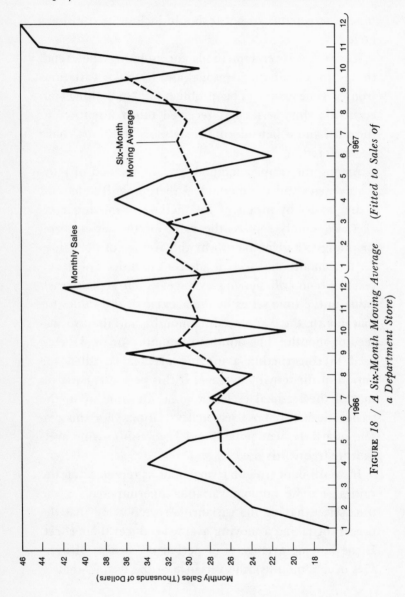

FIGURE 18 / A Six-Month Moving Average   (Fitted to Sales of a Department Store)

the variance of the random component of the resulting moving average—will be reduced to σ^2/n. In Figure 18, we show a 6-month moving average fitted to a time series, showing the consequent reduction in variability.

The method of regression is another method of removing seasonal and irregular variations from a time series so as to isolate the trend. Here, we fit a straight line or other appropriate curve to the time series in an effort to represent the trend. The method used for fitting a straight line is the same one exactly that was described earlier in this chapter, where we fitted a straight line to the relationship between the Index of Industrial Production and the GNP.

Although the method of regression has some statistical appeal, it is difficult and sometimes dangerous to apply. The primary difficulty lies in not knowing what kind of a trend curve to fit to the data. If we simply fit a straight line, extrapolation of this line to predict a future value of this time series (which is our underlying reason for doing a time series analysis in the first place) may have disastrous consequences.

Once the trend has been isolated, perhaps by one of the methods described or by other, more sophisticated methods, there are several ways in which the original time series can be "detrended" so that seasonal variations can be separately estimated. One method consists simply of subtracting the trend value from the original time-series value. The resulting time series will be trend-free, showing only seasonal and irregular variations.

A second, and preferred method, is called the *ratio-*

to-trend method. It consists of dividing the original data, month by month, by the corresponding trend values in order to create an index series. If we multiply each of these ratios by 100, we can think of the resulting index series as a time series of percentages of trend. Such a series is trend-free and, if we have a long enough series, we can also free it of irregular variations. For example, if we have a four-year time series, we can average the 4 percentages of trend for January, the 4 percentages of trend for February, and so forth, producing 12 "average percentages of trend," one for each month of a "typical" year.

There is some debate over which type of average should be used, the mean or the median. As we are taking the average of a relatively small number of observations (four in this case), the mean could be unusually influenced by one or two outlying observations (possibly caused by a tornado, a bookkeeping error, etc.), and it is usually preferable to use the median for this purpose.

Once we have estimated the trend and we have constructed an index of seasonal variation, we are in a position to make some kind of a prediction of a future value of the time series. This prediction, of course, is subject to two general kinds of error. First, and perhaps most serious, an incorrect underlying assumption about the trend (the wrong mathematical model) or the emergence of a new development that could cause a future change in the trend can result in a completely incorrect prediction. Second, even if the underlying model is a reasonably good description of the true economic world, we are at the mercy of irregular variations or chance variability.

Irregular or chance variations do not present nearly as serious a problem in prediction as incorrect estimates of the trend. Once the trend and seasonal variations are removed, we can estimate the variance of the irregular variations. Based on this estimate, reasonable limits of accuracy can be prescribed for future predictions, on the assumption of a current model. However, we should not be misled by possibly small error limits produced in this way. It is important that we remember that we *assumed* the form of the trend and that we check our assumptions by every means possible. In addition, we should continue to monitor these assumptions in the future, continually revising our predictions as we refine our model.

Summary

In this chapter we have emphasized the dangers and the difficulties inherent in making economic predictions. But important and far-reaching decisions are made on the basis of such forecasts, and without them businessmen could make no intelligent plans for the future.

If the day ever comes when perfect or near-perfect economic predictions can be made, we shall at last have found ourselves living in a utopia. In the meantime, we can take our choice. We can rely on the ouija board and the tea leaves, we can rely on hunches, or we can rely on statistical methods of forecasting *reinforced by sound business judgment.*

Regardless of which method we choose, we can go broke or we can make a fortune. Somehow it seems wisest to use the best that modern science has to offer, to use it with intelligence and understanding, recognizing its advantages and its pitfalls, and hoping all the while that continuing improvement in theory and in method will provide us with an ever-improving basis for rational economic decisions.

Bibliography

Index

Bibliography

The following are reference books on sources of economic data:

Coman, E. T. *Sources of Business Information*. Englewood Cliffs, N.J.: Prentice-Hall, 1949.

Hauser, P. M., and W. R. Leonard. *Government Statistics for Business Use*. 2nd ed. New York: Wiley, 1956.

These books contain further examples that show "Statistics never lie but statisticians sometimes do."

Huff, D. *How to Lie with Statistics*. New York: Norton, 1954.

Moroney, M. J. *Facts from Figures*. 3rd ed. Baltimore: Penguin, 1956.

Wallis, W. A., and H. V. Roberts. *Statistics, a New Approach*. New York: Free Press, 1956.

The following introduce some additional ideas of probability:

Goldberg, S. *Probability, an Introduction*. Englewood Cliffs, N.J.: Prentice-Hall, 1960.

Levinson, H. C. *The Science of Chance*. New York: Holt, Rinehart and Winston, 1950.

The following give the mathematical foundations of statistical theory:

Freund, J. E. *Mathematical Statistics*. Englewood Cliffs, N.J.: Prentice-Hall, 1962.

Hoel, P. *Introduction to Mathematical Statistics*. 3rd ed. New York: Wiley, 1962.

Mood, A. M., and F. A. Graybill. *Introduction to the Theory of Statistics*. 2nd ed. New York: McGraw-Hill, 1963.

These books and pamphlets deal with index numbers, their use and construction.

"The Consumer Price Index: A Short Description of the Index as Revised, 1953." Washington, D.C.: U.S. Department of Labor, January 1953.

Fisher, I. *The Making of Index Numbers.* Boston: Houghton Mifflin, 1923.

Mitchell, W. C. *The Making and Use of Index Numbers.* Bulletin 656. Washington, D.C.: Bureau of Labor Statistics, 1938.

Mudgett, B. D. *Index Numbers.* New York: Wiley, 1951.

Snyder, R. M. *Measuring Business Changes.* New York: Wiley, 1955.

The following introduce various methods for analyzing economic time series and making economic forecasts:

"Adjustment for Seasonal Variation." *Federal Reserve Bulletin.* Washington, D.C.: Board of Governors, Federal Reserve System, June 1941.

Davis, H. T. *The Analysis of Economic Time Series.* Bloomington, Ill.: Principia Press, 1941.

Newbury, F. D. *Business Forecasting.* New York: McGraw-Hill, 1952.

Prochnow, H. V. *Determining the Business Outlook.* New York: Harper & Row, 1954.

The following are textbooks in the field of business and economic statistics that have received widespread recognition and that are aimed at the introductory reader:

Croxton, F. E., and D. J. Cowden. *Applied General Statistics.* Englewood Cliffs, N.J.: Prentice-Hall, 1955.

Freund, J. E., and F. J. Williams. *Modern Business Statistics.* Englewood Cliffs, N.J.: Prentice-Hall, 1958.

Neter, J., and W. Wasserman. *Fundamental Statistics for Business and Economics.* Boston: Allyn and Bacon, 1956.

Richmond, S. B. *Statistical Analysis.* 2nd ed. New York: Ronald Press, 1964.

Index

A posteriori probability, 31, 71
Arithmetic mean of price relatives, 144
Arrival rate, 88, 92
Average, 28
  moving, 163
  weighted, 139
Axioms of probability, 60

Bar chart, 11
Base period, 134
Bayes' rule, 66, 130
Bayesian estimate, 131
Bayesian inference, 129
Bell-shaped distributions, 22, 93
Bias, 104
  of nonresponse, 127
Binomial coefficients, 81
Binomial distribution, 78–87
  mean of, 86
  standard deviation of, 86
Bureau of the Census, 4
Bureau of Labor Statistics, 4
Business cycles, 161

Categorical distribution, 16
Central tendency, 27
Chain index, 147
Chance, 53
Charts
  bar, 11
  pie, 9
  statistical, 9

Chebychev, P. L., 50
Class, 16
  frequency, 34
  interval, 19
  limits, 17
  mark, 18, 34
  modal, 23, 30
Coding, 35, 37
Coefficient of determination, 158
Coefficient of linear correlation, 159
Collateral information, 70
Comparisons in series, 134
Computing formula for the variance, 47
Concomitant variation, 159
Conditional probability, 64
Confidence limits, 116
  for proportions, 126
Consumer-price index, 136, 146
Correlation, 156, 159
Criterion of least squares, 153
Cumulative frequency distribution, 19, 23
Cumulative percentage distribution, 20

Decision criterion, 120
Decision making, 53, 102
Dependent variable, 153
Descriptive statistics, 4
Determination, coefficient of, 158
Deviation, 42

Distributions
  binomial, *see* Binomial distribution
  categorical, 16
  cumulative frequency, 19, 23
  cumulative percentage, 20
  curve, shape of, 22
  frequency, 16, 27
  normal, *see* normal distribution
  numerical, 16
  percentage, 20
  Poisson, *see* Poisson distribution
  probability, function, 77
  skewed, 29
  symmetric, 30
  unimodal, 30

Econometric methods, 160
Economic forecasting, 161
Economic time series, 160
Elimination, Rule of, 69
Equal likelihood, 58, 63
Event, 60
  compound, 61
  disjoint, 61
  independent, 65
  logically certain, 60
  logically impossible, 62
  simple, 61
  trials of, 78
Experiment, 54, 73
Extrapolation, 15, 156

Fitting a line, 150, 165
Forecasting, economic, 161
Frequency, relative, 11
Frequency bar chart, *see* Histogram
Frequency distribution, 16, 27
Frequency table, 16

General law of addition, 62
General law of multiplication, 65
Geometric mean, 30

Geometric mean, computation of ungrouped data, 33
Graph, 11

Histogram, 21, 29, 39
Hypothesis, test of, 118

Income statistics, 30
Independent events, 65
Independent variable, 153
Index
  chain, 147
  consumer-price, 146
  of industrial production, 137
  of seasonal variation, 166
  weighted, 145
Index number, 133
  base period for, 134
  comparisons in series of, 134
  consumer-price, 136
  price, 133
  price, calculation of, 143
  simple unweighted, 144
  weighted, 142
Inference
  Bayesian, 129
  statistical, 54, 103
Intercept, 153
Irregular variations in time series, 161

Least squares, criterion of, 153
Life Insurance Fact Book, 11
Line, fitting a, 150, 165
Line, trend, 15
Literary Digest, 105

Mathematical model, 156
Mean, 28
  arithmetic, 28
  computation of grouped data, 34
  computation of ungrouped data, 32

Mean (*continued*)
geometric, 30
sampling, distribution of, 180
weighted, 30, 139
Mean deviation, 42, 45
Median, 28
computation of ungrouped data, 33
Mil-Std 105D, 83
Modal class, 23, 30
Mode, 23, 28
Moving averages
method of, 163
period of, 163
Multivariate statistical analysis, 160

Negative skewness, 23, 31
Nonresponse, bias of, 127
Nonsense correlations, 159
Normal distribution, 93
area under, 95
mean of, 93
probabilities, 96, 100
standard deviation of, 94
table of areas, 98, 99
Numerical distribution, 16

Ogive, 23, 25
Operating characteristic curve, 121
Outcome of an experiment, 54, 73
"Outliers," 31, 42

Parity ratio, 137
Pascal's triangle, 82
Percentage distribution, 20
Period of a moving average, 163
Pie chart, 9
Poisson distribution, 88
mean of, 92
standard deviation of, 92
table of, 91
Population, 4, 103
Positive skewness, 23, 30
Price index, 133
calculation of, 143

Price relative, 133
arithmetic mean of, 144
weighted mean of, 146
Prior information, use of, 129
Prior probabilities, 66, 70, 130
Probability, 53
a *posteriori*, 71, 131
axioms of, 60
conditional, 64
equal likelihood, 58, 63
fundamental laws of, 60
general law of addition, 62
general law of multiplication, 65
prior, 66, 70, 130
special law of addition, 61, 76, 81
special law of multiplication, 65, 81
unconditional, 64, 70
Probability distribution function, 77
Proportions, 123
confidence limits for, 126
estimation of, 124
sampling distribution of, 125
unbiased estimate of, 125

Queuing problems, 92

Randomness, 73, 80, 88
Random sample, 54, 73, 104, 106
Random variable, 73, 103
Random variation in time series, 161
Range, 41
Ratio-to-trend method, 165
Regression
method of, 163
Relative frequency, 11, 55
method of, 56
Residual variance, 158
Rule of Bayes, 66
Rule of Elimination, 69

Sample mean, 107
  distribution of, 108
Sample, random, 54, 73, 104
Sample space, 59, 74
Sampling distribution, 109
  mean of, 111
  of the mean, 112
  of the median, 115
  variance of, 111
Sampling distributions of proportions, 125
Sampling, survey methods, 128
Sampling, systematic, 106
Scatter diagram, 151
Seasonal variation, 56, 162
  index of, 166
Secular trends, 161
Shape, of a distribution curve, 22
Simple unweighted index, 144
Skewness, 23, 29
  negative, 23
  positive, 23, 30
Slope, 153
Smoothing a time series, 163
Spread, 41
Standard deviation, 45
  calculation of, grouped data, 45
  interpretation of, 48
  See also Variance
Standard units, 49
Standardized variable, 101, 121
Statistical charts, 9
Statistical decision making, 102
Statistical hypothesis, 118
Statistical inference, 54, 103
Statistical tables, 8
Statistics of income, 30
Subjective probabilities, 59
Symmetric distributions, 30, 93, 101
Systematic sampling, 106

Tables, frequency, 16
Tables, statistical, 8
Tally, 18
Test of an hypothesis, 118

Time series, 160
  business cycles in, 161
  random (irregular) variation in, 161
  seasonal variations, 162
  secular trends, 161
  smoothing of, 163
Tree, 69, 130
Trend lines, 15, 161
Trials of an event, 78
Type I error, 118
Type II error, 118

U-shaped distributions, 23
Unbiased estimate, 114
  of a proportion, 125
Unconditional probability, 70
Unimodal distributions, 30
Unweighted index numbers, 145

Variability, 41
Variable, 153
  dependent, 153
  independent, 153
  random, 73, 103
Variance
  addition of a constant, 45
  calculation of ungrouped data, 44
  computing formula for, 44, 47
  multiplication by a constant, 47
  residual, 158
  See also Standard deviation
Variation
  concomitant, 159
  seasonal, 56

Weighted average, 139
Weighted index, 145
Weighted mean, 30, 139
  of price relatives, 146
Weighted price index, 146
Weights, use of in economic indexes, 142

ABOUT THE AUTHOR

Irwin Miller is a senior staff member in the Management Sciences Division of Arthur D. Little, Inc. and Adjunct Professor of Statistics at Boston University. He was formerly Professor of Statistics at Arizona State University and has a broad background of private consulting experience in statistics, applied mathematics, and related fields.

Dr. Miller has published in The Journal of the Royal Statistical Society, The Journal of Applied Physics, The American Statistician, *and other journals. He is coauthor of three books,* Manual of Experimental Statistics *(1960),* Algebra and Trigonometry *(1962), and* Probability and Statistics for Engineers *(1965).*

A NOTE ON THE TYPE

The text of this book was set on the Linotype in Baskerville. The punches for this face were cut under the supervision of George W. Jones, an eminent English printer. Linotype Baskerville is a facsimile cutting from type cast from the original matrices of a face designed by John Baskerville. The original face was one of the forerunners of the "modern" group of type faces.

Composed, printed, and bound by The Colonial Press Inc., Clinton, Mass. Designed by Leon Bolognese.